The Way I See It

Bob Starrett

For Liz:
All the Best Keep hoping
for a better world
Bob Starrett

First published 2013 in Great Britain by Fair Pley Ltd, Glasgow.

ISBN: 978-0-9575997-0-3

An archive of Bob Starrett's cartoons is held at
Glasgow Caledonian University Archives.
Further details available from -
Carole McCallum (University Archivist)
E: C.McCallum@gcu.ac.uk
T: 0141 273 1188

Typeset by The Print Register Ltd

Printed by Bell & Bain, Glasgow

For Dunky Lamont

A working-class intellectual

Contents

	Page
Acknowledgments	7
Foreword	13
The Electric Blanket	15
Billy Scott's Walk	20
The Buffer's Tale	21
The Applicant	23
The Pig's Tale	24
On Location	26
Joe and the Store Man	33
Below Decks	34
Rainbow Coalition	35
Romance	36
Bunty	37
The Naive Painter	38
Pugwash and the Fluorescent Tube	39
The Daft Rigger	40
The Olympics	41
The Trials	42
Find the Tim	43
The Hand	44
Deck Painting	46
Glasgow Smiles Better	47
Alpha and Omega	50
Are you listening?	52
The British Sense of Fair Play	53
The Plate of Iced Buns	55
Your Number Is Up	56
There Was a Man...	63
The Film Fan	69
Two Anomalies	70
A Reasonable Man	71
The Birthday Cake	72
The Meeting	75
The Singer	79
White Christmas	81
Paddy at the Barras	87

The Paperhangers 88
Clash of Culture, or what? 90
Had Brush and Did Travel 92
The Milk Carton 95
The Worried Men 96
All Life Is Here 97
The Two Take-Ons 99
A Housepainter Remembers His Swinging London 101
Bobby Goes to Hollywood (A Jock's adventure in Tinseltown) 105
A Wee Heat An' That 111
A Friend In Need Is… 113
The Man Previously Called The Blade 116
Venceremos 119
The Karate Kid 123
The Frozen Moment 126
The Kitty 129
To Err Is But… Keeping Warm 131
Once Upon A Time 136
Rhesus Negative Blood Group 141
The Field 143
The Scotsman, Irishman, Londoner and Australian 148
The Journey 159
Jimmy The Barber 165
A Night to Remember 169
The Jump 173
It was Christmas Day… 177
Starrett on Italy 190
Doon Through The Years 194
Showing A Way 196

Acknowledgments

For my wonderful partner Lindy, who has fed, clothed and loved me for over twenty years, continually nagging me to 'write it down'. Her constant encouragement has been invaluable, as has been her extended family.

For my lifetime friends (note, NOT old friends) Davie Cooper, Jimmy Cloughley, George Kerr and Arthur Johnstone and their exciting, intense debating style.

My dear friend, the poet and educationalist, David Betteridge, who continues to educate me.

To the lovely Anna Chancellor who cheered up my terminally sick sister, wee Pat, and educated me in doing so. I should also mention Stevie the Concierge who robbed her as she lay dying of cancer; that taught me something too.

A big thank you to my *cara amici* in Fertigliana, especially Piero and Franco who with their industry and knowledge of country living have enabled this wee Maryhill man to survive.

Also Matthew and Sue for great evenings of poetry, art and great food.

I would like to mention my mentor, Dunky Lamont, a working-class intellectual and someone with that truly great gift of being able to distil extremely complex political events into concise, humorous format. I owe him a lot.

I've mentioned George Kerr above, but he really needs a section on his own. George has kept all of the stories for years in his attic and that takes some doing because his wife, May, having the tidiest house in the world, would have had them out ages ago.

John Usher who manages, without getting too mad, to keep me functioning in the 21st Century technically. Someone once said that 'I could cope if there were no moving parts'. This is so true. For instance these stories were all written in longhand and had to be brought up to speed *(typed on a computer – Ed)* by Alice Lister and Stephen Wright.

Thanks to Ken Smith, Tom Leonard, Chris Bartter, Mike Holmes and Carole McCallum for comments on the early drafts.

Thanks to Nick Trumble for design and layout.

Thanks to Carole McCallum, archivist extraordinaire at Glasgow Caledonian University, for sourcing many of my old cartoons.

Thanks to UNITE the Union, STUC, UCATT and GMB.

Special thanks to Sanjay Kumar at Praslin Pictures.

Thanks also to Jim Lister and Stephen Wright of Fair Pley for having the chutzpah to publish my work.

Most importantly, a heartfelt thanks to all the men and women who worked alongside me in shipyards, building sites and film construction, who supported me and managed to cover my stupidity and ineptness, enabling me to earn a living. They will never know how much I'm indebted to each and every one of them. I hope they, and all the new friends I've yet to meet on life's journey, will find something to enjoy in this collection and hopefully everyone is inspired to write their own stories.

'It's coming yet, for a' that'

Bob Starrett

London, February 2013

Bob Starrett's work illustrates the determination of UCS and their families, it reflects the struggles that were fought and won during that time AND are being fought today. His work is also a timely reminder of our responsibilities; responsibilities acquired from those that fought before us. 'The Way I See It' is an important document in the story of the on going struggle for Industrial Democracy.

Tony Benn

~ ~ ~

Francis Seneca McDade, the hero of John Byrne's Writers Cramp was described as 'poet, philosopher, painter, sage'. Bobby Starret is all of these and more.

I first met him as he painted a bunny on the back door of an ice cream van on the set of the 'Comfort and Joy' and from that day to this he has been a unique presence in my life and the most generous of critics. Nothing escapes the questing eye and pencil of this man from Maryhill and I'm delighted his stories are out and about where they belong.

Bill Paterson

~ ~ ~

A lifetime association and friendship with Bob has always been re-inforced by his total integrity, and his multi-talented personality, humour and good nature.

His contribution to working class struggle has been immense, and his dedication to the survival of not only the Clyde Shipyards, but also British Shipbuilding continuity, has been of profound importance.

A true son of the Clyde working class and a sound friend.

Davie Cooper

Clyde Shipbuilding Worker

~ ~ ~

Bob Starrett epitomises the all too rare precious link between workers and artists.

I first became aware of Bob's work during the historic UCS work-in when he was the official cartoonist for the Bulletin produced by the Co-ordinating Committee to keep the workers informed of developments at every stage.

As a member of the Communist Party, involved in the campaigns of solidarity with refugees following the military coup in Chile, anti-racism, against nuclear weapons, unemployment, etc, I witnessed the creative, inspiring role played by Bob and the other artists from theTrade Union Centre Poster Group in all of these struggles.

I have a great affection for "Rattling the Cage" politically and personally - as a descendent of Irish immigrants whose grandfather, father and uncles all worked in the shipyards - I could relate closely to its politics, humour and anger.

I worked as secretary to the General Secretary of the STUC and really welcomed their recognition of the importance of Bob's work, in sponsoring the "Race Against Time" anti-racist exhibition and distributing "Rattling the Cage" to all STUC affiliated organisations.

Two words I'd use to sum up Bob Starrett - talented and principled.

Pat Milligan

~ ~ ~

My first contact with Bobby was in the 1970s. The Communist Party had a poster group that I and several others were involved in. We used a lot of his cartoons in posters and leaflets. His cartoons were always brilliantly drawn and full of sharp social commentary. He must have produced dozens, perhaps hundreds, of cartoons for the Party and the movement. A good cartoon is often worth hundreds of column inches of words and it can explain complex ideas to many people who simply don't read much. The other essential attribute of Bobby is his sense of humour and his skill as a raconteur. Just last week I met him in the street with two other guys, and the banter was superb. It kept me going for the rest of the day.

Alan McKinnon

Former Chair, Scottish CND

~ ~ ~

Bob says " We walked with giants. "

For many years I have walked with Bob and, although he is not a tall man, I have always found that I have looked up to him.

David MacLennan

Producer (Playwright)

~ ~ ~

I first met Bob around the celebrations for the 30th anniversary of the UCS work-in and here at Glasgow Caledonian University Archives. We have been using his cartoons as a research resource ever since. Bob has generously given me copyright clearance for his work and has added to the collection over the years. The cartoons offer immediate visual impact and humour to many of the themes covered in our labour and trade union archives and will continue to act as a learning and teaching resource. Sitting hand in hand with our written resources, they will be preserved for the use of future generations in their quest to understand and interpret Scotland's rich labour and trade union history.

Carole McCallum

University Archivist, Glasgow Caledonian University

~~~

Bobby Starrett, my lifelong friend, has kept me entertained and informed over 60 years, (the Maryhill gene pool team). In the early days, searching second-hand book shops in search of knowledge. His continuing quest to try and better society is shown through his contribution to working class culture. *By creating we think* (Patrick Geddes) aptly describes Bob . He has followed this edict in his pursuit for Socialism.

This contribution of his captures vividly observations of workers' humour at work, play and their resilience in their day-to-day lives, often in hostile conditions.

Jimmy Cloughley

~~~

Artists and writers often stereotype. Starrett never does. His welders and engineers are real people. You can recognise them. During the UCS dispute his cartoons were an essential part of the armoury of the work-in. They exposed the bombastic Heath and the dithering Mr Davies and gave participants confidence in their own strength and that of their class. Starrett's work is a true example of how a Communist artist can contribute to the struggle for a better world.

John Foster

Secretary, Scottish Morning Star Campaign Committee

~~~
~~~

As Secretary of the Scottish Immigrant Labour Council, I organised anti-racist, anti-fascist meetings and concerts. Our aim was to build solidarity between the Indian and Pakistani communities and the trade union and labour movement. We produced anti-racist leaflets and publications including a wee publication called 'Equality'. Central to it were the satirical cartoons of a shipyard worker called Bobby Starrett. He was also a leading light of the famous CPGB Poster Group whose elegant posters graced many a demonstration. No matter how close to the publication deadline Bobby never said no and always produced the goods.

Maggie Chetty

~ ~ ~

The fun, the craft, the politics, and above all the Art. Welcome to the world of Bob Starrett - brilliant work!

James Kelman

~ ~ ~

Many cartoons by Bobby Starrett were published in the 1970s in Challenge during my time as Editor. I continued to use his work for the Anti-Apartheid Movement in Scotland.

His cartoons were well-drawn, witty and politically sharp. The cartoons reflected Bobby: artistically talented, humorous, astute, quick-witted and left-wing.

I recall the cartoon (Challenge, July 1973) in which he depicts Prime Minister Edward Heath grabbing a paint-brush from President Nixon against a background of their various scandals (Watergate, Lonrho etc). The caption read, *"Sorry, Dickie, but I need the whitewash more than you."*

It was a pleasure to know and work with Bobby as a friend and comrade and it is excellent to see his work published as a book.

Brian Filling

Former Editor of *Challenge*

Former Chair, Scottish Committee, Anti-Apartheid Movement

Presently Honorary Consul for South Africa in Scotland

~ ~ ~

Foreword

It is a long time since I commissioned Bob Starrett to paint murals in my Pub in Paisley Road Toll in 1975. I had been in the Pub around a year and Bob would sometimes stop in with one of his old mates Willie Bruce. The Bar was badly in need of a lift so this idea sprang up from Bob to do murals on the walls of the Bar and the theme was the best Select Football World Team ever. I held a competition with all the regulars to see who could come up with the team nearest my selection and it created quite a stir and arguments as there is nothing better than debate on which player was better than another. At the end of the competition Bob got down to doing all the paintings and they were brilliant and were a great focal point of interest when anyone came into the Bar. Years later when I renovated the Bar completely the paintings went missing. No-one knows how or who got them, but someone somewhere may be sitting on a few pounds of value with them.

Bob, as time has gone by, proved himself a very talented man, extending his ability through painting to writing stories which have a thread of his life and his own experiences of a Glasgow man's conviction in his beliefs, which are indelibly engraved in Bob's life. His loyalty to the working class is the badge he has worn all his life. There is no better root for Glasgow humour than the shipyards, but also it is a place to capture the human frailties of a Glasgow man's enduring endeavour and determination, and his capacity to laugh at himself. Bob captures these traits derived mainly from his own experiences.

It has given him a foundation of humility which has served him well; it is not easy to keep your feet on the ground when success hits you. I see it all the time and to quote a well-known Glesca saying – 'your heid's nippin' – could now be associated with Bob.

I wish his work a huge success and also that he is in good order.

Sir Alex Ferguson CBE

P.S. "Wha's like us?"

SOAP
THIS WAY UP
STARRETT

The Electric Blanket

The pipe insulator removed his face mask and lit up a cigarette, coughing violently as he did so. The painter stood in front of him holding out two twenty pound notes in his outstretched hand. The insulator waved him away with a gesture indicating he was aware of the painter and the proffered money, but there was a more important task on hand, namely to get an intake of breath.

When the spasm of coughing finally ended the insulator wiped the sweat from his face, shook his face resignedly, and looked at the painter who was already speaking: 'You should pack in the fags,' he said.

'Ah know, Ah know,' mumbled the insulator as he sat down on a drum of toxic material that he was using to lag the pipes of the ship.

The meeting was taking place aboard a ship being built in one of Glasgow's legendary shipyards. Fibreglass dust was everywhere and could have been seen dancing in a shaft of sunlight; if sunlight could ever have penetrated into the hell of metal and pipes that is the centre of a modern vessel. Sunlight? Aye, in your dreams.

The aforementioned pipes are the reason that the insulator has been employed. His function was to cover them all, mile upon mile, with asbestos tape and cement from his drum. This gunge he calls 'monkey dung' – a light-hearted term for what is causing his ferocious coughing and is killing him.

'Right, young man. What can I do for you? A single or double? Blue or floral?' wheezed the insulator. As he did so he extinguished his cigarette.

'Gie me a double please…eh, floral', replied the painter.

The insulator stood up and produced a dog-eared notebook from the top pocket of his overalls, causing a small dust storm around him as he did so. Absent-mindedly he brushed this from the notebook, took a pencil from where it was stuck between his head and his helmet, and wrote down the painter's particulars.

'I'll see you on the deck above about three, OK?' the insulator concluded.

The painter nodded in agreement. The insulator took the notes, stuffed them into the notebook, replaced the pencil, pulled on his face mask, pulled from the side of his belt the incredibly sharp knife that is the insulator's preferred tool and commenced working.

'Single or double what?' enquired an electrician sitting nearby, tying thousands of electrical cables into groups and inserting them in metal trunking.

'Eh, what?' mumbled the insulator through his mask, noticing the electrician in the gloom and dust for the first time.

'It's electric blankets son. Nae rubbish neither. It's ma wee seam. Are ye interested? If so, gie's yir name an' cash an' yir declared in'.

The electrician approached the insulator, enquiring if the products were a good deal.

'Aw half-price seconds, but nae substandard crap!' replied the insulator.

'Right, Ah'll huv a single,' declared the spark.

'Could ye no' huv asked me when the painter was getting fixed up?' said the irritated insulator, stopping work, replacing the knife and restarting the trading procedure.

'Oh, aye, an' make it floral,' exclaimed the spark.

As the transaction was nearing completion, they were joined by a young foreman.

'What's this, eh? IKEA for fucks sake! A nation of shopkeepers, right enough.'

The electrician had returned in haste to the cable tying. The young foreman, noticing the alacrity with which the spark had resumed work, could hardly contain his anger.

'If you're not happy working in this industry pal, and you would rather be blethering on the outside, that can be arranged. Just you get cracking wi' your cables or you and I will be taking a walk upstairs.'

The electrician was by now working at such a speed he had already cut his hand on the metal trunking, but who cares. He wasn't being taken to the Manager's office and, in any case, he had just negotiated a good deal into the bargain.

The foreman, seeing the effect he had just had on the electrician, experienced a surge of power and in a flush of excitement turned to the insulator. He addressed him in sarcastic tones, 'I think you're in a wee bit of trouble squire'.

Almost before the sentence was complete the insulator had pulled out the blade and held it point uppermost under the foreman's throat. This type of knife is almost entirely comprised of blade; the handle is merely a piece of tape wound round the end. The business part is razor sharp; being kept in that condition by being sharpened every thirty minutes or thereabouts. Now it's under the young man's throat with an angry insulator on the end.

The foreman is now silent. Beads of sweat are on his forehead and upper lip. He is on tiptoe, stretching with every sinew to rise even higher. His arms are outstretched for balance. Comically, as he stretches further, his white helmet – the symbol of his authority – falls from his head and rolls under some machinery. He is terrified.

Building ships is a dangerous occupation, but the dangers are known, understood, and accepted with a kind of fatalistic logic that lessens the fear. This knife business is something else. The foreman's muscles ache, but he daren't weaken. That knife is sharp.

The insulator speaks in a rage, teeth fastened with spit. He mockingly repeats the foreman's threat:

'You think *I'm* in a wee bit of trouble squire? Well, you're fucking dead right on that score, an' ah mean DEAD. I've got about a year tae live, wi' this daft asbestosis – an' you say you think I'm in a wee bit of trouble. FUCK OFF out of my sight or I'll blade you right now!'

The knife removed, the young man makes a rush for safety.

The insulator is coughing again as he composes himself.

The electrician has been working conscientiously all during the dramatic encounter. Jobs are scarce, so why draw attention to yourself by even being involved in the incident as a witness. He had been lucky already with a warning – don't push it. But having heard the performance he is intrigued. He is human. He speaks up.

'Is that true what you said about you only having a year…?'

He couldn't bring himself to finish the sentence. It seemed so final, but he ploughed on.

'I mean, the doctors – they could be mistaken…the wrong diagnosis…' he trailed off.

After a period of silence, he resumed.

'There's something I have to ask you. Can…'

The insulator butts in to save the spark further embarrassment and confusion.

'Aye, I know, but this time they're spot on. I've had every test there is. It's hopeless. Seen a' the specialists. I've been in an' oot that hospital like the lobby light. See when they first tell you the news, you don't take it in. Aye sure, you know what it means, but you don't want tae…believe it…you just shut down your thinking part, then you think: 'Why me?'…then you think: 'Well, why no' me?'

'Then you plan that trip round the world. You know the score spark. Everyone says the same crap – 'if it wiz me, I'd rob a bank an' leave the money tae my family.'

'It's no' that simple. How would you go about robbing a bank? I wouldn't know how to begin. An' there's the in-laws to contend wi' – they've hated the fact that the wife married me in the first place. So, robbing a bank is a non-starter.

'The thought of dying scares the shit oot o'me. I lie awake nights wi' that one. I've nae answers. It's sore. That's why, in a way, I sell the electric blankets. It's a way of putting some cash aside for the wife. It's a scam, but naebody gets hurt. An' when I'm gone she'll have enough for maybe one o' the cruises, you know.

'Ach, I'm running off at the mouth again. I'm sorry, but that's why I come to work. It keeps my mind off the future - you know, lying in bed wi' the big daft oxygen bottle beside you…I'm fucked…and I'm worried…but here, you were wanting to ask me something. What was it?'

'Can I change it for the blue?' the electrician said.

Billy Scott's Walk

Billy Scott was walking through the yard in his usual plodding, measured fashion. He was wearing the painter's brown boiler suit and his hands were in his pockets.

The foreman, known unaffectionately as 'The Rottweiler', spotted him and, incensed with anger, rushed to confront Billy. This was something that gave The Rottweiler immense pleasure. Stabbing his finger at the painter he spat, 'Move yourself! Go a little faster will you?'

'This is a boiler suit, no' a tracksuit' Billy nonchalantly replied, and continued without changing his gait.

The Buffer's Tale

The metal buffer took off his mask, wiped his sweat-streaked face with his sleeve, put down his screeching buff and lit a cigarette.

He looked round in the semi-dark of the engine room and nodded to the two others who shared this part of the ship with him. They were glad the buffing machine's dreadful noise had stopped, if only for a few minutes, even if it left behind the ghost echo, like a sound in a seashell. They nodded back and quickly got into conversation, without any of the preliminaries that most other social groups effect. The reason was simple enough; any moments of relative quiet had to be taken advantage of, as in a shipyard such moments are few and far between.

'Jesus, it's hot doon here' said the buffer as an opener.

'Naw, it's no'' one of the others, a welder, said from out of the semidarkness. 'Ye should feel the heat o'er in that Spain – that's whit ye ca' heat!'

'Spain, did ye say? Said the buffer. 'Is Burma any good tae ye? An' whit aboot India, eh?'

'Were ye there then?' the welder enquired.

'Aye, I was, many years ago. I was wae the Chindits, y'know. Wingate and a' that. I can see it the noo as I'm talking tae you. Ye've no' seen nothing 'til ye've seen that daft jungle. It's the darkest green and aye wet. You think we've goat rain here? You should see the monsoons! An' see oot there, the stars are bright as anything – like a lot o' new shillings in the sky. No' as bright as the stars frae the troop carrier mind you, but maybe they only seemed brighter 'cos yer happier oot on the deck o' a boat instead o' building wan.'

'Hiv yous no' seen the Irrawaddy river at a'?' he queried. 'No' even at school? Christ, the forgotten army, right enough! We waded across it wance, chasing the Japs…wait a minute…I'm a wee liar. The Japs were chasing us, but no matter. That river is magic – aboot three times as wide as this wan'. He nodded at the hull in the direction of the

Clyde. 'An' full o' queer-looking fish tae. See in that jungle, there are millions o' birds o' every colour in the rainbow. An' see you, painter' he pointed at the painter. 'You'd go aff yir heid trying tae mix up a shade anything like them. Same wi' the flooers, but they're a' poisonous, so they're bad news.'

He sighed and looked at his near-finished cigarette. 'Some days I can see it so clear in a' its Technicolor, that I'm there, y'know.'

The painter, having been brought into the conversation, turned to the buffer and smilingly said, 'If you won the pools and you had the dough tae go *anywhere* in the world, where would you go?'

The welder and him exchanged winks as they waited on the reply.

'Anywhere in the world, ye said?' questioned the buffer, as he slowly took a last draw on his cigarette.

'Aye!' chorused the other two.

'I'd be away doon tae London like a shot. It's fuckin' magic!!'

And with that he replaced his mask and the dreadful noise commenced again.

The Buffer's Tale

A TALE TOLD DURING A FIVE MINUTE LULL IN THE BUILDING OF A FRIGATE

The Applicant

The shop steward was standing outside the shipyard handing out leaflets for the Communist Party. Heading in his direction the eccentric character known to all in the yards as "The Talking Horse" approached. "Talking Horse" announced that after giving it some thought he was now ready to join the Communist Party. With lightning speed the steward exclaimed 'Sorry, we're full up.'

The Pig's Tale

In an industry as dramatic as shipbuilding there were a great many 'personalities', but one celebrity stood out as the master – the famous "Pig" McCrindle. He worked as a burner in the Fairfield's yard, Govan and was a patter merchant of truly legendary status.

His phenomenal talent was put into good service during the historical Upper Clyde Shipbuilders' Work-in. As the thousands of workers waited to hear the latest developments from their leaders – the two Jimmys, Reid and Airlie – the "Pig" would entertain them and boost the collective morale.

I would argue that it was not an insignificant contribution, and indeed may have been more important than anyone understood at the time.

One of the reasons the Work-in was different from most other forms of industrial struggle was that it had an infectious 'feel-good' factor that spread outwards from the yards and embraced all other sections of society. When any industrial action is depicted by the media it is so po-faced and humourless that it doesn't engage our emotions. It's reminiscent of a freezing cold shower in the morning. Undeniably, it's good for you and is the right thing to do, but…well, you get the point.

Much of the Pig's repertoire could be classified as politically incorrect, but, like anything, it has to be judged in the context of the period and his audience.

This is one of his routines:

The Pig's Tale

It was one o- thae dark mornings in the middle of winter. The sleet is crashin' against the windae frames – y'know the kind o' thing.

Ma heid is burstin' – I'm ill – but really ill. I've overdone it the night before.

The alarm goes aff – she gies me a kick. 'Get up you', she says 'or you'll be late'.

I manage tae put ma foot on tae the cold floor. Am no kiddin' yous,

I'm ill. I manage to find the workin' boots and struggle to put them oan.

I put the right boot oan my left foot an' then I dae the same thing wi' the other one.

I sit on the edge of the bed tae get ma wits aboot me – heid nippin'.

She leans across and gies it –

'Ya daft eejit ye – they're oan the wrang feet!'

'Dead right there, hen. They should be oan your feet!'

On Location

For far longer than he could remember it had been 'Wee man', 'Tam', 'Hey you', 'Jock', 'Johnny', '251607269' (this was his army number, or so he claimed). He said that even when drunk he could remember it. In truth, he had served in the armed forces all of twenty-four hours. He had not even unpacked when he decided a soldier's life was not for him, preferring to travel without the dubious benefit of a uniform.

Yes, it had always been 'Hey you', 'Scotty', 'Mac', 'Glasgow' or 'Jimmy'. Of late he would answer to 'Sweaty'. This set Tommy's teeth on edge, being the feeble cockney rhyming slang for sweaty socks = jocks – 'Oh, leave it out'.

Tommy was a well-travelled wee guy from the west of Scotland. He had faked his age on so many official documents he was hard pressed at times to remember his actual age. Anyhow, let's just say he talked about the moon landing as if it was the recent past. He had worked on oil rigs, civil engineering projects, housing schemes, hydro-electric dams and in the shipbuilding industry. He had painted bridges, gasometers, pylons and palaces, both in the United Kingdom and overseas. He had always been involved in hard physical work and had the muscles and aches to prove it. He, like many others, had been constantly on the move looking for The Main Chance, The Big Pay-Day, The Elusive Prize, The Turn. He could quote from that bible of all itinerants 'Songs of a Sourdough' and would do so frequently (Robert Service was always with him on his journeys):

'If I could find myself a proper groove
What a deep mark I would make!
So I chop and change and each fresh move
Is only a fresh mistake'

But today was different.

He was somewhere in the Dorset countryside on a luxurious dining coach on a film set. 'On location' they called it. He had been on location, one way or another, all his working life, but not like this. He was surrounded by well-spoken young ladies who had adopted him, after their fashion.

Probably he carried some rarity value being a product of your actual proletariat, a true blue collar to them. As good Greens, all endangered species were sacred. The only other working class person that they would have had any contact with would be the woman who cleaned their mother's house. Sure their lives were spent in taxis, but black cab drivers are something else again.

Today there was excitement abroad. He could feel it being generated by his friends, and so infectious was it , he couldn't resist becoming a part of it. 'On location'. He smiled as he said it to himself. He let himself relax for the first time in ages.

In most of the places where he had laboured it paid to keep your guard up. Some guys took such liberties. What was it about all that stuff? All in the past though now. He was 'on location'. New scenery, new friends, new people to meet in local shops. He had heard it all when he had gone in for his cigarettes that very morning.

'I'm with the film unit – Sorry I'm not at liberty to divulge the title – The actors? Oh yes, you can speak to them – as a matter of fact I...etc., etc.'

You can make up your own dialogue - most of them do.

One of 'his' young ladies brought Tommy a bacon roll on a paper plate, another his tea and yet another leapt up and got him a paper napkin. Tommy had never experienced such attention. Well, there was that time in the Scottish Highlands when the landlady had made a bit of a fuss, but that was years and years ago – 'What was her name again? It used to come to...so easily – tip of my......ach it's not important – now is what matters'.

And what a now. The girls crowded in on him as he ate, one even had her arm round his shoulder in a proprietorial manner, the smell of her ubiquitous Barbour quite excited him.

He regaled them with jokes, stories, lies, anecdotes and tales of the incidents and the variety of characters that he had encountered on his journeying. They laughed gaily, loud and often – and why not? They exhibited the finest whitest teeth that their parents could afford. He could not have been more impressed. He was a bit shy of his full quota himself, having lost many through neglect and the remainder owing to being a shade too slow in defending himself in the noble art. None of this mattered a jot in his home port of Glasgow where, because of the soft water and high sweet intake, having a full set usually referred to a set of dentures.

Tommy was vaguely aware that he should be working, but was assured by everyone there that it was better to remain where he was.

A new scene was being set-up. This entailed everyone of importance on the film being in attendance. The director was there of course, and his assistant; the lighting cameraman and the camera operator; the production designer and his assistant. Also there was the script supervisor and, of course, her assistant. Tommy was only too aware of keeping the head down at times like these. At the appropriate moment when the grown-ups had completed their deliberations the gaffer would tip him the nod that the art director was on her way and it would be wise for Tommy to be on parade. Ready. He was on the payroll as the Appalachian scenic painter. The reality was less glamorous. He would be expected to transform a room or such like in the quickest time available. It often included employing all the skills Tommy had acquired through the years.

At times he could be called upon to paint a mural in the time it would take his designers to down their cappuccinos. To do this he would use the fastest drying materials and would work in a sweat producing pace more akin to the aerobic exercises favoured, he knew, by his female followers.

Yes, he was working in the film industry, but in truth he was a decorating hit-man – 'just hit it and leave – like yesterday', they were fond of saying.

In the meantime the more girls laughed, the funnier Tommy's yarns became. He told the one about Joe - his own favourite - he had to clean up a few of the stories and remember not to be so free with the curse words.

He couldn't understand why he did so as his audience swore constantly.

Somehow it sounded so different to him coming as it did out of those finest whitest teeth he had ever seen. He was enjoying himself – and the girls couldn't get enough. Had he been a dog he would have wagged his tail – he wasn't, but he would have loved to have been.

Pam was laughing with that deep laugh of hers. Sure it was part a by-product of her smoking habit, but what the hell. Tommy wished he had spent his life like this instead of knee deep in shite on some bridge construction.

'Strange that'. He wondered to himself how these girls abbreviate their names to the minimum - Pam, Al, Eff, Jo – was it a condition of employment? All had signed their contracts using their full names, though Pam had used two hyphens whereas the rest made do with one.

Al was insisting on yet another tale from the shipyards. How they all loved the quaintness of the language used in that particular industry. The especially enjoyed 'plater', 'caulker', 'hauder-oan', 'red boy' but their favourite was 'the double bottoms'. This they never tired of hearing and Tommy based some yarns in that part of the ship even if it had taken place in an entirely different industry.

'These docks must have been fun places to work.' Jo said this. Mixing up docks with shipyards annoyed Tommy but he let it pass, to them it was all interchangeable, just something the working classes did – bless them. They understood enough to know that industry of that type was noisy, smelly, dangerous, lowly paid and not terribly important, unlike the film industry.

It has been humorously said that in the Italian navy everyone is an admiral, such is their fixation with rank. The film industry needs no lesson from anyone in this field: Tommy's girls were no exception. One was a second assistant (that is to the director); another a third. Then there was the 'coordinator' and lastly, but in no manner least, Pam a line producer. Heaven help the person who called any of them 'runners'. This was only slightly less of a crime than calling them 'dear' or 'love'. Tommy had had to learn this quickly...

All thought of themselves as fairly democratic individuals and knew the script off pat. 'Save the rainforests, dolphins, Antarctic, endangered tribes etc., etc.' Two were vegans, the others vegetarian, 'I never eat anything on a plate that looks up at me'. All preached equality, but of the St. Augustine variety 'Not yet O Lord, not yet'.

The coordinator never tired of telling other members that Tommy was a 'sweetie' a 'real puppy dog'. This slightly concerned him as some members of the crew were riggers and electricians – bears like himself who might want to test how far the puppy dog could be pushed. He knew that game inside out and back to front, but it didn't worry him too much, he was now a favourite of the girls. And he wouldn't mind being pushed by any of them.

The gaffer banged his fist on the coach window indicating that Tommy should join him a little distance from the vehicle. Reluctantly he left the warmth of his young audience. Putting his arm round Tommy's shoulder, he whispered in his ear that his squad of electricians had 'dropped a bit of a bollock'. For the last scene they had taped cables along the top of the wallpaper in the room of the house, and when de-rigging they had ripped the paper. Could Tommy use his decorating skills and solve their problem?

'There's a drink in it for you, Tom' the gaffer informed him. 'No sweaty today then' thought Tom. A liquid lunch on offer – 'This beats the 'dry' oil rigs any day'.

'You're on', he said.

Tommy entered the house and viewed the damage. In the 'ideal world' that everyone spoke about on a film set, he could easily mend the damage. Down to the local wallpaper store, check out the pattern books, buy a roll and proceed to 'feather' it to make the tear invisible. But not now. Any second now his designer would be calling for him. He must help the electricians, what if the director noticed the damage, what if the lady whose house it was returned, what then? In a semi-panic Tommy took stock of the situation. Firstly, where would the previous decorator have left any leftover wallpaper? Of course, as everyone knows, the paint goes under the sink. But wallpaper. 'What if?' In an instant Tommy was in the cupboard under the stairs and as quiet as possible, not to arouse anyone, he rummaged around the detritus.

Working in darkness he could hear the voices of the crew going about their business. Pushing aside the unused exercise bike, and the equally unused rowing machine, his hand felt the familiar shape of a roll of wallpaper. Bingo. So far, so good.

At that moment Pam appeared at the door. The light blinding him for a moment, he squinted in her direction and before he could explain the circumstance she angrily screamed, white faced:

'What do you think you're doing? Answer me this minute. This is some decent person's home. How would you like a stranger prowling through your things? Soiling everything you touch.'

With white flecks on her lips she screamed into her two-way radio 'Jason – Pamela here, could you pop through for a second?' Gone was the fake cockney accent, it was now replaced by her clear-cut, upper-class accent, with every word enunciated precisely. Tommy shook his head, baffled by her change in demeanour, and attempted to push past her. She grabbed him with a Barboured-arm and again yelled into her Motorola 'Jason quickly, he's getting away!'

Jason arrived almost at once and tried to make sense of the situation. Through the aforementioned finest, whitest teeth imaginable she spat out her accusations.

Jason was a pleasant, soft, nice, creative guy who always took the easy option, and he did so again. Glancing at the anger in Pam's face he demanded an explanation from Tommy.

Tommy silently shrugged.

How could he explain his actions without putting the electricians' mishap centre stage? Call the gaffer to account, who, to save himself, would offer his squad up for dismissal? Tommy had never played the Judas role; he wouldn't start now. He knew how it would end, and it did. He was expelled very quickly from the location. Jason, without looking at Tommy, gave out the usual platitudes about his money being sent on etc., etc.

Tommy made his way from the site avoiding the coach windows. He need not have bothered, his fan club were now gathered around Pam intent on her every word. They were discussing the forthcoming epic that was now 'green lit' and Pam had a say in who would be in the crew. Tommy? He was history - gone. A replacement was already on his way to the location.

It was raining now, a fine drizzle. As Tommy headed away from the area and towards a bus stop he glanced back at the collection of vehicles belonging to the unit.

Waiting for the bus that would take him to the nearest town, Tommy rolled a cigarette. He once again found solace in poetry:

'Ha ha! He is one of the Legion Lost;
He was never meant to win;
He's a rolling stone, and it's bred in the bone;
He's a man who won't fit in.'

Joe and the Store Man

The ex-paratrooper Paint Department store man was in his element doing what he could do well, which was leaping over a guardrail which was about 20 feet from the hard cement floor. Landing, as he had been taught all those years ago, on his head and rear end, he rolled over and jumped to his feet ready to climb the stairs and repeat the performance for the benefit of the watching painters, who encouraged him on to greater feats of aerial dexterity. That is all except Big Joe who was languidly cleaning his brush over an oil drum. Occasionally he glanced at the proceedings. Joe took a drink, and for all his unkempt appearance was a well-read bachelor of the old school. He also had come through the war and there wasn't much anyone could teach Joe about human behaviour. As the painters bayed for more and more of the storeman's acrobatics I sidled up to Joe and indicated the performance.

'What about that, Joe?' I asked.

'Oh, that's nothing,' he replied. 'I do that every Friday night.'

Below Decks

There was a monetary award for the more confined spaces that you could find yourself in. My mate was a great guy, but it was known to everyone that he loved extra payments, for whatever reason, and it was often joked that he would have worked the two-minute silence.

One day we found ourselves fitting out a frigate in the James Watt dock, Greenock. We were working well below the water line in a very cramped space. I enquired what would happen if the ship caught fire. How would we get out?

At that moment a siren blasted out.

'You're about to find out, let's go.'

We left everything behind: paint pot, brushes, sheets, etc. and scrambled up the ladder to the next deck then repeated the exercise several times until we were on the corridor leading to the exit. The floor was ablaze and the flames periodically lit up the air above. The tiles which were made of thick plastic were well alight and the adhesive added to the mixture. We ran back the way we had come and my mate's knowledge of the ship's layout enabled us to get out to safety.

'What if this happens during a war and all the lights go out as well?'

He shrugged.

A few years later this ship was in the battle for the Falklands.

Rainbow Coalition

The long hours of unrelenting boredom were one of the hardest things when painting a ship, especially if it was being executed in the depths of a dull Scottish winter. Add to this the fact that we had been months and months working with battleship grey paint, so periodically anything to break the monotony was to be welcomed, any incident.

This is such as example.

The 'high heid yins' were making the rounds as was their custom when a vessel was nearing completion. The party was made up of various members from the NATO alliance resplendent in their uniforms. 'Full regalia will be worn'. As they ambled towards the ladder leading to the bridge they had to pass us. Our wee trick was to stand with our backs against the bulkhead that was still to be painted, leaving a small space for the grownups to pass. The various admirals, captains, and other ranks passed us. As we had our paint pots and brushes held in front of us, they pressed themselves hard against the already painted bulkhead getting their uniforms covered in the grey paint. They never noticed this, paying too much attention to presenting a serious expression to us the lower orders.

They were now assembled on the bridge and looked a frightful sight. At first they laughed and pointed at one another unknown to them that the back of each man's uniform was covered in paint. The worst of the lot was a Dutch Commodore who being last also had his heels painted as he ascended the ladder.

The deed done, the two of us made our escape to another part of the ship. Then laughed at our childish prank.

'Well that passed a few minutes' said my mate. Not long to go now to lousin' time'.

The moral - don't have grown men performing repetitive work months on end.

Romance

Possibly not the most suitable description but it will have to do.

The way the departments were set up there was always an overlap in the designation of tasks. For instance, when a ship was nearing completion the painters would be adding the finishing touches and the cleaners from the clean ship department would be working in tandem. As that department was nearly one hundred per cent female invariably romance flourished. Attraction between adults can arise in the most unusual of places, so to find a couple giggling like teenagers together aboard a boat was no surprise. Incongruous as it seems, romantic encounters were part of the folklore of the yards, and the painters were more than happy to oblige. It is always good to be of service to one's fellow workers and being part of something that helps to break the monotony made all the participants feel good.

One painter's romance caught the attention of another painter who preferred his escape method to be in a glass. He was baiting the first guy who had fathered eleven children with his wife.

'What are you thinking of going wi' one o' thae cleaners? Hiv you no' got a wife at hame?'

The man replied: 'I have but we don't see eye to eye a' the time, sometimes we don't talk for ages. We're on an' off.'

'Aye, that's as maybe, but you must have been on and off a few times - at least eleven.'

Another time a painter's token of his feelings was given to his cleaner. The following day she arrived with a beautiful black-eye. You don't have to be a Sicilian to appreciate heightened emotions. It's the same in dull grey Scotland.

Bunty

Wee Bunty and her team had finished the half-bottle and now having the flavour were in the humour, but the well was dry. Bunty volunteered to get the cargo replenished. She approached the painter and asked where he kept the turps. Carefully she filled the bottle, replaced the cork and caught her foreman's eye for a pass out. She went up the road to the off-license and demanded the shop assistant smell the contents.

'I bought that this morning and I've just opened it. I don't know about you but it smells a bit funny to me.'

The man removed the cork and inhaled, reeling back he conceded that something was amiss. Bunty returned to the squad and, properly refuelled, they worked away at their tasks in hand. This time singing as they did so.

The Naive Painter

All morning the banter had been of a high quality, both in content and delivery. The cleaners were in good spirits (no pun intended) and at intervals the painter noted the half-bottle being surreptitiously passed among them.

He was washing down the bulkheads, a boring and cold task this freezing winter as the bucket of water remained as cold as it had been on being issued that very morning. Now the incoming horn blew for the dinner break. They all left the ship, not exactly reluctantly, but a part of them not wanting to bring an end to a pleasant episode and they returned early back to the ship to continue the work.

After dinner the painter was called away to another part of the ship for an urgent job and on his return to the section that was to be finished he dipped into the pail and exclaimed:

'How can that water be warmer than it was and the day is even colder?'

One of the cleaners replied, 'Maybe someone has poured his flask into your pail.'

'Still, it's a strange thing – hot water'

'What planet do you come from?' another of the women said, and they all exploded with laughter.

The painter blushed, his stupidity now being the subject of the afternoon mirth.

Pugwash and the Fluorescent Tube

Pugwash was one of those people who got a kicking on a regular basis. His *modus operandi* was to approach a couple drinking in a pub and declaim to the man: 'Is that the only old cow you could find to have a drink wi'?'. The kicking inevitably followed. The talk in the painters' hut was that he must have a drawer full of black eyes as he invariably came in on a Monday morning with one eye shut.

So to sum up he was thought a bit stupid but this wee event I witnessed could prove differently.

He approached the gateman security officer.

'Listen pal I'll be coming in fae Asda wi' a fluorescent tube when I come back in aff dinner time so I don't want a pull'

'Nae bother ma freen – noted' said the gateman.

Pugwash then returned to the paint shop and propped up a flori tube ready for the off that night. He then rolled up an empty flori cardboard case and put it in his overall pocket.

When the dinner time came round he went out the gate and waved to the gateman who noted it.

Once outside he unrolled the empty tube and straightened it out. Holding it stiffly he entered the yard and with a lot of gesturing indicated his 'purchase' to the gateman. At night it was a simple case of placing the tube in the container and walking out. I thought this scam was the height of ingenuity and intelligence and yet come the following Monday there was Pugwash with his usual black eye.

The Daft Rigger

We're sitting in a cafe outside Fairfields.

Cooper, with the lace out of his boot yet again, attempts to teach me the knot. I'm baffled. Time and time again he deftly ties and unties the salt cellar.

'Got it?' he repeats.

'Just once more. I want to be certain.'

'This is the simplest knot known to man' he patiently explains. The horn sounds for a return to the yard. 'Have you got it now?' he enquired anxiously.

We split up and go aboard our respective boats.

I'm working aloft in the engine room and my task as an engineer's helper/rigger is to lower a section of piping over a makeshift handrail to the deck below and the waiting engineers. I look over the rail.

'All ready?'

They nod. I tie the rope to the handrail - 'Now is it one turn or two?' I think to myself as I place the rope round the pipe and launch it from the deck. The last thing I see is the worried face of the engineer as the pipe rushes towards him. He is carted to the Southern General and I feel guilty being unable to understand knots and ropes.

A coda. My uncle Jimmy received an M.B.E for his expertise in rope-making in the Gourock rope works.

The Olympics

Glenn McFibber, obviously not his real name but more apt than the one he has, was in full flight. He is one of the legendary patter merchants that the yards have been famous for. He declaimed in a hoarse growl:

'Take they Olympics – nothing but war games tidied up. Thae Greeks used it to get their young men ready for the next scrap. A' that throwin' the javelin, spears mair like. Now take running – oh aye the running. As soon as the black team got intae it, now being better fed, the game was up. So they switch smartly to the next thing – dressage. Dressage fur fuck sake – naebody in ma street has a horse, far less the time tae train wan for dressage.

'But wait - haud oan. When we dae finally get intae the dressage they'll be a move ahead. Oh aye never underestimate that lot. They're already ahead. For the next Olympics they've introduced a new game: 'Throwing the Platinum – bring yer ain platinum'.

The Trials

The boat had completed the major part of the undertaking. The Citadel test, where the boat tilts over at a 45% then returns to the upright position, had been completed and was marked up accordingly.

The tomahawk missiles had been test fired and now it only had to give the Olympic's engines a clean bill of health and return from the measured mile at Ailsa Craig, or as it's affectionately called Paddy's milestone, positioned as it is out in the Irish Sea.

The job was completed, most of the work undertaken and everyone was A1. A holiday feeling crept in to the squad who had been working non-stop, round the clock since the vessel left the yard. A small celebratory drink was being shared out below decks with much laughter, tiredness and the sheer relief of nothing major to be attended to before the handover to the owners.

A young foreman thought that this would be a good opportunity to exercise his authority and lay down his claim as a disciplinarian and hence advance up the power structure.

He hammered on the cabin door where most of the laughter was coming from. No answer. He hammered away, louder this time, getting increasingly agitated, his face grew redder. Eventually a bear opens the door and through bleary eyes enquired 'What can I do for you pal?'

The angry foreman points to his head and declares 'You can stop all this nonsense for a start' and that's the power *this* gives me. Sad to relate he had forgotten to put on his white helmet (the sign of authority). His red face turned away from the door but not before the bear swore that he saw the beginning of a tear start to form.

Find the Tim

The ship, which shall remain nameless, was classified top secret; this being the period of the cold war. It was all a nonsense, of course. The Russian fishing fleet being constant visitors to our waters and the punters availing themselves of cheap holidays in Bulgaria and resorts on the Red Sea. But the charade has to be played out and by stamping the legend 'top secret' it ensured that the job would be performed to the highest standards and there would be no rush to finish the work – the taxpayers picking up the tab.

The game was being played out for the visiting 'glee club' admirals, commanders and captains from the various navies of NATO. The British contingent was proudly showing off the quality of the vessel and with their usual disdainful demeanour towards their allies and emphasising how secure and secret was everything. They were all crowded into the operations room where the 'war' would be orchestrated from if and when the war broke out.

There was a lull in their procrastinations when through the public address system came loud and clear the distinct cry:

'7...1...Celtic seven and the Huns one!'

The embarrassed British contingent were red-faced with anger.

'Find that man at once, 'shouted an admiral.

Who could have been the delinquent? All that they had to go on was he was a Tim. In a labour force of thousands it would be an impossible task to find the culprit. Top secret? Aye, 7-1.

The Hand

The price of brass was on the up. The scrap dealers were paying top price so it was on some people's agenda.

I was working in the 'Lea during this period. The brass portholes and covers were being stolen and it was obvious it had to be someone with access to the vessels who was stealing them.

I'm getting on with my work when another guy appears at my side: he begins unscrewing the porthole. What to do? He works away methodically, oblivious to my presence. He whistles tunelessly as he dismantles the heavy brass cover when suddenly the whistle changes pitch. The cover has come down on the back of his hand and as it is a watertight fit, it is absolute. His hand is neatly cut right through. He takes stock of his situation and stops the bleeding with his hanky. It's soaked through so he picks up a piece of dirty sacking I was kneeling on. Indicating for my silence he handed me the sacking.

'Tear that intae strips painter, be a pal eh?'

I hesitated, then did as he requested. He was in agony. He bandaged his hand then instructed me to make a tourniquet and I tied it on his arm. He then sat down.

'Ye huvnae got a smoke on ye, hiv ye painter?'

'No,' I replied.

'Just my fucking luck it's wan o' thae days' he said.

'Should you not go to the ambulance room for that hand? Maybe I should go for help?'

'Naw, you just get your wee brush oot and get oan wi yer work. We don't want anyone coming in here, right'. He was in and out of consciousness. The pain was acute.

'Are you sure you don't want me to get someone to have a look at it?'

'You kiddin? The minute they see this injury they'll hunt fur the place it happened an' when they see the blood I'll be fucked'. He moaned and groaned hour upon hour until finishing time. He stood up in severe pain.

'Thanks pal – made it'. He then set off and joined the other workers leaving the yard.

I never saw him again, but I know that some guys can withstand extreme pain if they need to, especially if they have been up to no good.

Deck Painting

Bobby was painting the deck with an artist's brush. He had been given it by the storeman and hurried out the paint shop by our ever angry gaffer on to the ship that was to be painted.

Now the gaffer, Sammy, was towering over him fuming. Speechless. Eventually he exploded in outrage.

'Are you fucking at it?'

Bob looked up through his glasses and pointed at himself.

'Me?'

'Aye, fucking you. Are you at it?'

Before Bob could reply Sammy had thrown off his dust coat and grabbed a roller from another painter. He tore a page out from the Daily Record – placed the page on the deck and carefully poured a puddle of paint on top of the paper.

'This is how ye do it – nae tray necessary. Now do it. And put that toy brush away!'

Wee Bob took a last puff of his pipe, then in a theatrical manner reminiscent of Stan Laurel, placed a page of the newspaper on the deck. Then he upturned a gallon of paint on top, it spread everywhere. Painters leapt for safety.

'Like that?' said Bob, looking at the gaffer. The gaffer, fearing that a heart attack was on the cards, quickly left the scene. Bob winked at the other painters, then slowly relit his pipe.

Glasgow Smiles Better

Glasgow – the biggest concentration of heavy industry outside of Germany. Birthplace of the most famous and largest ocean-liners ever built – the Queen Mary and Queen Elizabeth. Home of the builders of railway systems and steam trains for the entire world. Centre of learning in the shape of Glasgow University of Lord Kelvin fame. The City visited by Mary Queen of Scots, Bonnie Prince Charlie, Robert Burns, President Jefferson and, during the second world war, Hitler's pal and deputy – Hess.

But all that was in the past. Glasgow changed its industrial function in the 80s and became the fun place to be. Newly opened wine bars were a feature of the city for the first time. Clubs flourished and the City fathers attempting to kill off, for once, the old 'Mean City' image, commissioned an entire campaign based around the cartoon character Mr Happy. To accompany this endeavour the slogan ' Glasgow's Miles Better' was painted on every available gable and appeared on all billboards. What Glasgow was miles better than was never specified, but it was assumed by many to refer to Edinburgh. But whatever it meant, the smiling yellow face of Mr Happy was everywhere.

Included in the campaign were a few of the City's single-decker buses. Painted in Glasgow's normal orange livery, they had attached to the front a huge plastic laughing face. It covered the entire front of the vehicle and cheered up the populace. On the side of the bus in dancing letters, read 'Your Wee Happy Bus'. With so much 'happiness' about, everyone felt obliged to look for fun wherever it could be found. It was difficult for some to come to terms with the post-industrial, non-macho, fun role. But being Glaswegians, they would give it a good try.

Anyhow, to our tale. The shipyard workers were all at their usual positions at the bar of their local pub. The talk was deadly serious, their usual banter stifled. No jokes this evening. The voices were lowered, which was a real effort as most of those assembled suffered from industrial deafness and usually conducted their conversations in a very loud manner with appropriate signs and actions. Tonight was an exception. The previous week one of their number had been killed in an accident at one of the shipyards. They were discussing funeral arrangements.

The one who handled the mutual aid fund was allocating the collected money amongst the others and stipulating the various functions associated with the burial. One of the men was delegated to book a hall somewhere accessible to them all. Another was to organise the pies, cold ham and such food that is traditionally consumed at these occasions. Another was to arrange the transport. Yet another was entrusted with buying the drink to ensure that their old mate got a real send off.

They all finished up their drinks and agreed to carry out their assignments with the due respect and dignity that was called for to honour their fallen comrade.

These were tough guys from a tough industry, but with hearts that were softer than many found in less dangerous occupations. And, although unaccustomed to the kind of endeavour at hand, they understood the importance of doing everything right.

The day of the funeral was identical to any other that ever took place in Glasgow. There was the overcast grey sky and the light drizzle and a cold wind.

The men stood around the grave awkwardly, dressed in their best suits. The turn-ups of their trousers were muddied and their once highly polished shoes were thick with fresh clay. Their large gnarled hands hung incongruously from the new shirtsleeves. Ties were knotted neatly but some of the men continually moved their necks from side to side, unused to the restriction.

Heaps of wreaths and flowers with all the usual messages of condolences were in evidence. The shipyard workers were waiting for the rest of the mourners and a few attempted gallows humour to try and lighten the proceedings, and maybe some of the grimness from the event, but with little success.

A collective sadness hung over the occasion. The dead man's family stood in a huddle a few yards from his ex-workmates, but shared silent nods of acknowledgement with them.

The undertakers shuffled their feet, waiting for the off. The Co-op minister, who was all things to all men and could cobble a sermon up out of the merest detail, was desperate for a smoke. He fumbled with the cigarette packet in his jacket pocket absent-mindedly, wishing it was all over. Where were the other mourners? Periodically but furtively, as if some shame was attached to this, one or other of the shipyard men glanced at his watch.

Time passed at a snail's pace.

Then some unknown force focussed all eyes at the cemetery gates. Coming through the entrance were two giant, rosy cheeked, laughing faces. It was gloriously uplifting. The faces approached the waiting mourners. It was then seen that the new arrivals were smiling – and why not? Written on the sides of the buses was the claim – 'Your Wee Happy Bus'.

The tension was broken.

All laughed in spite of themselves. Even the bereaved family joined in. Someone remarked that this is exactly what the dead man would have wanted. And it was true – he would have. The man who was last to join in the laughter was the man who had been put in charge of hiring the transport. He was in a state of acute embarrassment, compounded by the sadness of the event. He lightened up when the laughter became so infectious that it became impossible to keep a straight face. Soon there was a bizarre sight of mourners standing round a grave with their arms around one another laughing hysterically. A wonderful feeling of collective joy swept through all the participants.

Aye, Glasgow smiles better – no danger.

Alpha and Omega

'First and Last' the pub's name
Now has a different connotation.
Not where my old man first took a drink
But certainly his last.
Ever the gallant he assisted two 'old' ladies across the road
He was struck on the ladyless return by the white van.
He lay there his life now locked in fast forward
No freeze frame – no replay for the ex-canecutter
Ex-cowboy, ex-this and ex-that.
War service he gave a miss because his unthinking brother
Putting a gun to his head didn't.
So now he drove along predictable lines to Auchenshuggle
Never to desire.
Agnostic – it wouldn't have been his first choice
To be comforted by a priest,
But cradled childlike in his arms he breathed his last.

A wee explanation about the piece above. The First & Last is a pub beside a busy Glasgow Road. My Old Man, having helped two elderly ladies safely across the road, was struck fatally by the white van being driven by a young man on his first day working. My Dad had been a tough guy cowboy in Australia in the 1930's and had reluctantly returned to be the breadwinner of his family, when his brother shot himself in the army. A consequence of this was my father was exempted from war service because there was 'insanity in the family'. My Dad was an atheist, having experienced a Catholic mother and an Ulster Protestant father. When knocked down, a priest from the nearby church rushed out and cradled my dying father in his arms. The irony of this is that I used to jest with him that when his time came I would send for a priest. Life is indeed is strange.

Are you listening?

£750, eh? An' we paid over a grand, no' that that seems tae bother you lyin' there covered in your sunblock. You're no' evening listening. Just gie you a deckchair, a wee bit o' sunshine, an' your nose in a book an' you're happy. Oh aye, nae bother. An' don't try an' kid me you've no been sleepin' cos I know you have. I've been away a dauner roon the boat fur hours an' you're at the same place in your book. I'm no' sayin' I'm no' enjoyin' it cos I am. A' I'm sayin' is they said that they only paid £750. Through the net. The net, eh? We're no' on the net so we're buggered. There is a big difference between £750 and £1250. If I hadnae known I'd have been happy. But, well, it niggles me. That's a'. It's still a good value whit we paid but they've got away wi' the prize. Are you listening? Great, init, how some people can just nod aff anywhere. An' that's another thing a' thae books you buy you cannae have read them a' surely. Even so you must know every story aff by heart by noo. An' if you're no' readin' wan o' them you're readin' the Record. An' it's a day auld, tae. An' the funny thing is in your paper the other day it said that lying oot like you do gies you the ballroom, an' you still dae it. That means that you don't even believe whit you read. But you maybe should. Whit colour are you tryin' fur anyway? Right I'm away tae hae a look down below. I'll see you. Are you listening?

£750. Nae harm tae them, but it's a right scunner a' the same. Oh, you're wakin' up at last tae join the livin'. I'm just back the noo frae ma walk an' I think we should book up fur next year, but you know we should dae it through the net. It's just a thought. You listening?

The British Sense of Fair Play

The young woman stood nervously in the dock. The lawyer had been attempting to get her to say what she had heard a youth shout during a breach of the peace.

'He said "Where's the effing dog?"'she stated. The lawyer smiled patronisingly at the woman then turned and addressed the judge.

'It is well known in legal circles your honour that you are a dog breeder of some standing'. The judge allowed himself a slight smile. The lawyer continued, 'But even you would have difficulty in placing this breed'.

The judge nodded.

Again the lawyer asked the woman the questions and again she repeated that the youth had shouted 'Where's the effing dog?'

'Can you be more specific?' he implored.

'Well you know,' she mumbled.

'Know what?' he baited.

'Y'know,' she shrugged her shoulder and her voice tailed off, embarrassed.

'That's the point, young lady, I don't know and I want you to tell me and the court what you really heard'. She nodded indicating that she had understood the request, then after composing herself said in a barely audible voice, 'Where's the fucking dog?'

The lawyer walked briskly towards the jury box. He put his hand on the old oak rail and winked conspiratorially at several of the female jury members, then turning to the girl he spoke in the manner of a General Practitioner on a house call. In his well-modulated voice he spoke:

'Now, all these good people here have given up some of their very valuable time to come and attend these proceedings to ensure that there is fairness all round. They're all tax-payers and like any normal people they want to see how their hard earned money is being spent. Therefore would it be too much of a liberty if I asked you to speak up?'

He leant forward still with his hands on the wooden rail. Joined the jury members, a trick he picked up from watching courtroom dramas on American television. The other hand he theatrically cupped to his ear. He indicated with a nod of the head for the woman to proceed.

Staring straight ahead, avoiding any eye contact, the young woman shouted clearly 'Where's the fucking dog?'

The judge clasped his hands to his ears. The lawyer shut his eyes and winced loudly. 'Now, now lass, we don't want to frighten decent people outside the building do we?' Mortified, the woman blushed and kept her eyes down, looking at the floor.

The lawyer smiled at the jury. Some of the predominantly middle class women returned his smile. It was all terribly exciting this, maybe even better than the last televised royal happening and would be a good topic at the next coffee morning in the church hall.

The lawyer waved the young woman to stand down. The clerk of the court restored order.

The judge glanced at his watched and picked up his papers. Everyone shuffled out of the courtroom. Jury members smiled one to another, their faith in the British Justice reaffirmed.

The Plate of Iced Buns

The Elderslea Dry Dock canteen was a true wonder to behold, and that's not a cliché. It was a wonder. Ten men sat at a long table – five a side. The serving woman came round with an enamel pail and dished out soup while taking the order for the main meal. The pudding – custard or jelly was on a plate on a ledge under the table. On top of the table were placed ten pieces of iced buns. When the meal was completed you all gave the woman 10p each. It was one hundred per cent efficient - what could possibly go wrong? Aye well, that old human nature again.

We all sat down, a mixed collection of shipyard tradesmen. A wild looking worker sat down and in a theatrical manner , with exaggerated gestures, proceeded to lick the icing off all of the buns. As we ate our soup everyone kept an eye on this man, wondering how to end this challenging behaviour, but not wishing to be the first into the fray.

That is all except one wee wiry guy who, without a change in his facial expression, plunged his fork into the back of the icing eater's hand and then, ignoring his screams, slowly got up from his seat and, without looking back, tossed a ten pence coin onto the table as he walked away.

Your Number Is Up

The turreted building was a leftover from the Victorian period. The communal corridors were hideously painted in two mind-numbing colours beloved of institutions everywhere. The upper parts of the walls were painted in a sour cream shade and the lower sections were a dark tan highly glossed. Overhead hung rows of dust encrusted fluorescent lights, which being faulty only worked intermittently. The overall feeling was one of hopelessness. If that had been the intention of the designer it worked more than could have been imagined.

The most obvious feature of the place though was an overwhelming eye-watering mixture of cheap industrial disinfectant, stale sweat, urine, testosterone and the stench of unwashed socks and undergarments. This informed that to 1000 men this was 'home'.

The men were, in the main, guys who followed the work. Tunnellers, steelworkers, asphalters, and itinerant agricultural labours. There were men who had toiled all over the world. Some had families, others were drifters, merchant seamen, oil workers. Ex-this and ex-that. A few low-lifers and many who were simply institutionalised.

A thing they all had in common was that they all slept in a cubicle that measured 6 feet by 5. It contained an iron bed, a wooden clothes rail, narrow wooden shelf and a small chipped ceramic sink in one of the corners. This last item was highly prized by all because it doubled as a urinal during the night-time hours. This was recognised by the attendants, but a blind eye was turned to the habit, as the worst crime in the place was to piss the bed. This act was usually punished by instant dismissal from the building so anything that served to avoid that was to be welcomed.

The other thing they all shared was that on the varnished oak door was stencilled a number in yellow paint. This was the most important thing in the building. This was how the residents identified one another.

Your number was you.

The regulars would discuss how number 9 had been barred for a week for allowing another to sleep on his floor, or how 900 was found dead in his bed, by 64, when he had visited to play a game of chess with him.

251 took all this for granted now. He had been resident in the place for some time and it had become a normal kind of behaviour.

He sometimes thought about that. As he made his way daily along the corridor, down the Victorian cast-iron spiral staircase, through the metal turnstile, past the mottled green tiles at the door and out into the metropolis. It was similar to a time-lock and returning at night the routine was reversed and when back in his cubicle it all seemed so ordinary. Inside the building the real world simply ceased to exist.

The place was terrorised by number 11, a stocky red-haired man in his early thirties from somewhere up north. He ruled by fear, borrowing from some of the inmates with no intention of paying back. He also robbed others and when he felt the occasion warranted it, dealt out terrible and bloody punishment. In this he was sometimes aided by two other low-lifers, 12 and 16, who adopted an opportunistic turn of behaviour. They allied with 11 in the first place to avoid becoming victims themselves, and for the other reason that they liked to share in the rewards from his crimes. An additional factor was the respect that they felt was theirs by their familiarity to 11.

In a place with more than its share of tough guys, 11 stood out as a cruel, nasty bully, a liberty-taker of the worst kind. Why, in such a place, was he allowed to operate unscathed? The simple answer was he was the toughest guy in the building; he could fight like fuck.

But to our tale.

In such a closed community there circulated the usual stories – how 21 had been a master mariner and had lost his captain's ticket by making out with the ship owner's wife as his vessel was crossing the equator. He was allegedly dressed as Neptune at the time and the act took place on his table in the first class dining lounge. Someone remarked that it brought a whole new meaning to the request from a captain to join him at his table. He was discharged and eventually ended up in his present situation.

75, it was claimed, had murdered a Jehovah's Witness who had talked a bit too long at 75's doorstep, causing 75 to miss that vital goal of the cup final. The irony was that during his term in prison he had himself converted to the same branch of religion and on his release, having being institutionalised; he could only live in a closed community. He bored anyone who had the misfortune to sit near him at meal times, by preaching the word. It was even said that he talked right through the cup final from beginning to end. Not everyone was bored by him of course. 63 and 86 were usually in his company but that didn't count for much as 63 was partially deaf and 86 came from somewhere in central Europe and hardly understood English.

Ex-champions of various kinds who had taken to the drink were just too numerous to mention, with the exception of 35, who it was said had thrown his famous battle with the American champion when he was ranked no. 1 in the world.

The current rumour was of a more mundane nature but no less fascinating to the denizens of the place. It was stated by some of the occupants – well, 176, 5, 83 and 42 – that 407 kept something valuable in that tin box he carried around with him at all times. It was true he never let it out of his sight. He placed it on top of the sink, in the row of communal sinks, whenever he washed. At mealtimes he sat at the table with one hand on top of it as he ate.

407 was invariably well turned out, his shoes were polished toe and heel and under the instep. He wore a dark suit and flat cap and the only bit of colour was in the very exotic silk scarf he wore on top of his collarless shirt. The scarf was tied in a 'docker's knot', some speculated that this had been his occupation before he retired. Maybe so, then again maybe not. He was visited regularly by his two grown sons. They were called 'the twins' – no numbers for them. Unlike the other more infamous duo, they were not really twins but just liked to dress in similar fashion, but what they did share was the same line of work. They were engaged in violence.

One day, the date is unimportant, but it was one of those damp autumn days when the light doesn't vary much in the entire day and nothing much is expected of the day.

That day was to be different though.

It was the day 11, aided by 12 and 16, took it upon himself to relieve 407 of his tin box. It should have been so easy but 407 put up a good show and consequently was badly beaten. His opposition to the robbery caused 11's adrenaline to kick in and, thus angered, he inflicted such dreadful injuries that it caused 12 and 16 to be a bit concerned. The outcome was that 407 was hospitalised.

The thieves took their prize to cubicle 200 on the 3rd; this was the empty room that they used as their den. There they proceeded to break into the old man's tin. When it opened 11 exploded into a rage and scattered the contents around the cubicle, screaming that this shit hadn't been worth the effort.

The 'shit' in question was a few old photographs of 407 when young with a smiling young woman and two baby boys, presumably 'the twins', and a military medal hard won on the beaches of Normandy all those years ago.

11, 12, 16 stormed out of the building to the nearest pub for a consolation drink, laughing about 407's obsession with his tin box.

Word of the incident spread throughout the building and everything was forgotten as the residents waited with expectation for the inevitable outcome.

And come it did.

There was a small group hanging around the tiled entrance when the twins arrived the following morning. On the wooden bench, next to the turnstile, sat 507, 94, 21, 816 and 420 as usual, but they were joined on that day by others too numerous to mention. Today was to be the day and the fever had infected everyone, including 35 who although he kept his views locked in his head, knew the feeling only too well.

11 made his way to the entrance without the slightest change to his sullen features. A fight is like jumping into a cold shower. Once the initial shock is over – it's business as usual. That first punch in the face, the initial familiar pain then settled down to the task in hand.

So 11 was neither rushing to the encounter, nor was he dragging his feet, whereas 12 and 16 were a bit apprehensive about the whole affair. They hadn't any friends in the building and if things went badly and 11 lost the decision it was a certainty that they would be beaten up too, and expelled from the establishment into the bargain. But what were the odds for that?

By now the entrance was so crowded that some of the punters had climbed up to the alcoves on each side of the lobby and attempted to share the space with their silent stone companions.

The twins methodically removed their jackets, all very businesslike. Next off came the ties. No point in giving your opponent the opportunity to strangle you. They folded their jackets neatly and handed them to 308, who having in the past served royalty, placed them carefully on the table in the attendants' kiosk, which was situated just to the side of the entrance. The attendant then locked the door, placed the key in the top pocket of his dustcoat and joined 308 and the others to watch the promised spectacle.

Bang! It was on.

11 jumped over the turnstile and immediately went in to the battle. He was very good, he put together combination punches and delivered them with the speed and skill that had made him prison champion when he had been a guest of her majesty. Straight lefts, left and right hooks, elbows, head butts, kicks, every part of his being was perfectly designed for this. He was a fighting machine and he was fearless.

The brothers responded in kind matching him blow for painful blow – in stereo.

After the initial onslaught the twins settled to the job in hand and commenced to systematically hand out one of the most savage beatings that any of the onlookers had seen. And those same watchers had witnessed, or taken part in, their own physical battles all over the world in mine, ship, oil rig or battlefield and were fairly knowledgeable in such matters.

To hear bones cracking and see soft flesh explode in front of you is disturbing, but it is fascinating also, so no one looked away. Time had no meaning either for the participants or spectators. This was naked aggression, Darwinian survival made real. Hearts thumped, blood throbbed through veins and rushed to heads. Breathing was deep and fast. It was truly awesome, not in the trivialised modern American usage of the term, but in the biblical term. The drama continued.

Bang. Bang. Bang. Bang. It went on and on. Eventually 11 lay on the mosaic floor, in a mixture of blood from all the combatants, but mostly his own. Like a bull in the slaughterhouse he writhed in agony in a soup of piss, spit, blood and yes, guts.

71 remarked, to no one in particular, that the scene reminded him of someone called Francis Bacon. 805 and 6 looked at him for a moment, baffled, then their eyes returned to the fight. The more 11 writhed in pain the more the turnstile and the onlookers' shoes got covered in the sticky mess. Then he sighed and lay motionless. It was over.

Seeing this, 12 and 16 made their escape. So fast in fact that they jumped from the nearest window which happened to be higher from the ground than it looked. 12 broke his ankle and 16 bruised his back severely. They were so terrified of the other residents that they lay in silence to avoid discovery.

One of the twins was admiring their mornings endeavour. The other, having signalled to the attendant for a towel, was cleaning himself. The attendant explained to the twosome that to cover himself he would need to phone for an ambulance for 11 and as it usually arrived escorted by the police they should make their escape from the battlefield.

They thanked him for his concern and as he phoned they got themselves cleaned and were just putting on their jackets when it stirred.

The slab of meat on the floor moved. 306 claimed he saw the eyelid open first, but 306 always saw things other missed, it was said. So no one took his observations seriously. But what was not in dispute was what happened next.

With a bestial snarl 11 rose and leapt on to the twins. The brothers, caught unawares, went down under an attack of raw violence. They were bitten, kicked and beaten by the slab of meat until the spectators couldn't tell who was who in the bloody soup.

Some spectators turned from the gore – but not many. You only see an event like this once in your life and you will want to remember all the details when you retell it over the years.

Everyone knew they had been a witness to the real thing.

The ambulance arrived to pick up 11 only to be surprised by him standing in the doorway pointing to two heaps groaning on the floor. He indicated that he needed no-one's help and struggled through the silent numbers towards his cubicle. The crowd parted to let him pass and watched as he lurched along the corridor. The only sound was his animalistic breathing.

The epic was the only subject of conversation in the following months, discussed in whispers in case 11 was nearby.

One day, at the row of sinks, 251 heard some voices discussing his financial position and how with all the overtime he was working his cubicle was worth a visit. Looking through the towel that now hid his face 251 was aware of 11 nodding in agreement with the plan. Later that day a holdall was hurriedly packed and an exit made. The door to cubicle 251 was left lying open.

There Was a Man...

Until fairly recently I worked in the British Film Industry. More accurately it should be called the London Film Industry, as it is staffed in the main by people who live within the confines of the M25. The positions of power are held by predominately middle class types who couldn't face a job in the city. There are a few fallen aristocrats, ex-pats, ex-public schoolboys, ex-girlfriends etc., but the vast majority of the labour force comes from satellite towns such as Uxbridge Ivor and Boreham (Boring) Wood. London overspill dormitory towns. The inhabitants, if not exactly born within the sound of the Bow bells, are at least born with the sounds of them whenever they hear them on some East end soap.

Their predominant culture is one of the unbridled acquisitiveness and selfishness, wanting, like children, to acquire all of the toys that our consumer society can spew out.

They envy those who have obtained the 'toys' faster and easier than themselves. The outstanding aspiration of most of them is to have collected a full set before the final whistle blows.

To this end they devote themselves ruthlessly and act out a materialist version of Malcolm X's dictum of 'by whatever means possible'. Winning the lottery is only one of the ways they dream of achieving this. Another is to rob some bank. Consequently bank robbers figure highly in their pantheon of heroes. They admire the lifestyle of the villains and look on these 'heroes' as 'outlaws'. Like these 'outlaws' they vote Tory almost to a man.

During many tea-breaks I have found myself in a minority of one in condemning such heroes as Ronnie Biggs, the Kray Twins and Mad Frankie Fraser etc. etc. My workmates were under the impression that those villains were true working class heroes and I was some softy. My heroes - James Connolly, Airlie and Reid, and the many more unsung - were genuinely received with bafflement. This is an oversimplification, of course, as London has had its fair share of Labour Leaders and courageous International Brigadiers, but my workmates would have been hard pushed to name any of them. Aye, even if they could have phoned a friend, so what?

Well it saddens me on two counts. First, it deprives today's young men of proper role models and secondly they admire and envy the values and philosophy of the gangsters. These hard men with their callous attitude must never be confused with tough men. Hard means uncaringly dishing it out, but toughness indicates that one can take it. I've met lots of tough guys on my journey and without wishing to introduce Kipling-esque tosh of the 'play up and play the game' variety I make no apology for celebrating workingmen who have put their toughness at the service of their class. They are my heroes. This is a wee story of a big man on Clydeside.

Our tale takes place in a shipyard during the winter period leading up to Christmas. It's that time of the year when the day light loses the battle with darkness and the sky mirrors the colour of bare cold steel.

Billy was known throughout the Clyde. He had worked in most of the shipyards that lined the river and in a tough industry of tough guys it was acknowledged that he was just that wee bit extra. Not for him any of the adornments by which today's young men advertise their machismo. No tattoos, piercings, ripped t-shirts or stylised boorish expressions. No need for such tomfoolery. He was a welder, a good one too, one of the self-styled kings of the river. A shop steward and fervent communist.

Growing up in the 30s, in a deprived part of a deprived city, Billy had been a bit of a handful. Some might say that this is a slight understatement. But even his critics would have to truthfully say that he had never taken a liberty. No bully, he never ducked a scrap no matter what the odds. This is a lesson for all those vicious muggers and mobile phone thieves and batterers of elderly women. There is no honour in putting superior physical strength into such sneaky endeavours.

But there is honour when true courage is manifested, be it intellectual or physical, when a moral stance against a real injustice has to be faced. As Billy would declare 'Run once – you'll run twice'.

The shipyards where our story is located are awesome places in which to earn a living. The scale of the whole operation involved in building a ship is gigantic. Everything is larger than life. The giant overhead cranes, fitting out sheds, and the ship being built. Inside the vast sheds giant steel plates are worked on by hundreds of skilled operators. As they work they produce a cacophony of sounds, screeches, whines, banging, hissing that collectively makes your head sing with pain, ear protectors losing the battle.

The welders throw grotesque shadows through the shed whenever they arc their torches. The fantastic shapes of the steel that is being prefabricated is...forget it, visit a shipyard yourself.

To attempt to describe the methods that men use to communicate to each other in such an environment is beyond my abilities.

The problem is partially overcome by lip-reading, signs, gestures and a comic pantomime of mimed obscenities. It would need an entire encyclopaedia in itself to interpret and appreciate the richness of the working class culture on display.

Billy emerged from the awkward position where he had been working. He straightened up, rubbed the circulation back into his legs, and stretched his arms. He had been working on a low hydrogen overhead weld. It had been extremely difficult to execute the work; Billy had had to remain static until the welding rod had completed its run. The irritating sweat that had been trickling down his neck could only now be wiped. The dust that had been choking him could now be attended to.

He lifted up his welding mask and stepped onto a section of the prefabricated deck and drew a deep breath in what passed for fresh air in such places, and expelled a ferocious arc of spit.

'Aye, not long now', Billy thought. He lit a cigarette from the welding rod. 'Christmas break and freedom, ya beauty'. He allowed himself the luxury of a daydream of how he would spend the time. First a pint in the Lismore in Partick, then walk out of the city and over the hills towards Drymen, stopping for another pint at the Carbeth Inn and the chance to heat the hands at the log fire. Finish the beer and set out up and over the Whangie, passing that valley where Rob Roy hid his rustled cattle, then the final stretch to the Buchanan Arms and the reward of a three courser, another pint and maybe a wee golden one. He laughed aloud, banged his thick welding gloves together, throwing more dust into the polluted fog in which he worked.

He was happy with himself and why not. He was an excellent welder, equal to any on the river. He and his wife usually took fairly adventurous holidays and spent on them. Aye, it would not be long now 'til socialism proved itself the better system. Looking round at the ship being constructed, he was proud of the industry and his part in it. To work on a ship, and the time it takes to build it, is a strange thing. The ship becomes like a well-known friend. Each ship has a character unique to it and one day on completion finally sails away, never to return...well I've seen grown men wipe non-existent dust from their eyes.

Billy marvelled at it all. The sheer amount of collective expertise involved in the industry made his communist heart leap. He looked up at a giant steel plate as it moved above him. It cast a shadow blotting out the winter sky. Hanging as it did by four steel hawsers attached to a ring at each corner of the plate. Those in turn were joined to a ring in the centre of the plate attached to a hook a metre long. This in turn hung from the jib of the crane by a wrist thick cable.

It was said that the crane operator, working in concert with the grounds men, could land a plate on top of an egg without cracking it. The sheer flamboyance of even imagining such a performance is outrageous but I myself have shared a can of tea with men who claim to have witnessed such an event.

The giant plate swayed lazily in a slight breeze. With the clouds moving behind it it was difficult to see what direction it moved or indeed if it was moving at all. The hypnotic effect lasted only a fraction of a fraction of a second. Crack! - one of the rings failed. Then in rapid succession two others snapped. It was so fast. Billy was out of time. Too late to move.

Down it came slicing through his boots and burying itself in the deck, edge on. It was held swaying by the remaining ring. Through clenched teeth he silently screamed. Useless to scream anyhow, it would have gone unheard in the overall noise. But in that unheard cry Billy said goodbye to the Lismore, Carbeth Inn and the Buchanan Arms. The best laid schemes of mice and men. His whole life didn't flash before him. There wasn't time, but he knew in that instant life would never be the same again.

The safety squad leapt into action. They all knew what to do and set about it with speed and professionalism. In all walks of life accidents occur, heavy industry has always had more than its fair share, maybe that's why Prince Charles never considered it an occupational option. Men ran from other parts of the ship, many hands helped Billy into the ambulance. This one held his gloves; another took his mask off and gently laid him down. Within 15 minutes he was in the A and E department of the nearest hospital, where the staff worked at their optimum speed to attend to Billy's horrific injuries.

The young nurses gently removed his pigskin welder's jacket and his incongruous childlike polka-dot hat and prepared him for the operating theatre. Billy fully understood what was required of him and played his part. No histrionics, no complaining. They were fellow workers, like him, highly skilled and through gritted teeth he mumbled his appreciation. He was surrounded by a whole team of medical staff as they went about their separate tasks but as 'part of the whole'. He marvelled at the similarity to his own industry. He didn't utter a sound. He surveyed the hospital. The young nurses had decorated the ward with all the usual trappings of Christmas. At the end of the ward they had put up a real Christmas tree. The walls were covered in paper chains made out of the different coloured appointment cards. Above, hanging from an old fluorescent tube, someone had hung a bunch of mistletoe.

The nurses, seeing that Billy was cooperating and being patient, warmed to him and joshed and flirted as they awaited the brief time before the porters would wheel him into the theatre. All the time Billy was looking up. He beckoned one of the nurses over to him. She hesitated before complying, having heard stories of all kinds of abuse, both verbal and physical, that hysterical pre-op patients have been known to engage in. Her colleagues pushed her forward. Billy pointed overhead then at his injured feet.

'Kiss me under the missing toes', he exclaimed.

She laughed out loud at the sheer gallusness of the statement, covering her mouth with her hand as she did so. Billy repeated it and soon all the nurses were laughing. He laughed loudly himself and repeated it yet again. More people laughed. He was still laughing when they gave him the injection. It was a shared moment. The best kind. No nastiness, no gangster cool. No belittling of others. A real tough guy.

Coda: On a good autumn day Billy can be found walking past Rob Roy's hidden valley, having refreshed himself at the Carbeth Inn.

The Film Fan

They were a sorry lot. They being the newly-captured prisoners of the Italian army. Having been told that the Italians were an easy opponent and being a crack Scottish outfit, it didn't seem right somehow.

Arguments sporadically broke out among them about why and how the outcome had come about.

The Italians had herded their prisoners into a large public room and to keep them pacified, after a fashion, until they could all be processed, they set up a large screen and projector. Almost all the by now ex-soldiers were really not in the mood for any kind of entertainment; thinking about what lay ahead and would they be in captivity for the duration of the war. And who knew how long that could last – years possibly.

The lights dimmed and on to the screen was projected Fred Astaire.

'Oh, brilliant!' a Glasgow voice rang out. 'Ah missed this when it was showing up the town!'

His mates looked at him dumbfounded, but some men live in the moment and he was one of them.

Two Anomalies

At Yarrows, the Clydeside shipbuilders to the Admiralty and to other nations, I witnessed two little incidents that, for me, summed up the human condition. The frigates built on the Clyde are unquestionably the finest constructed warships anywhere in the world, so the two following anomalies stand out against the run of play.

Once a sophisticated piece of very top secret apparatus was being lowered into its position on the particularly specialised vessel. The various heads of department stood around watching, with clipboards and technical drawings in hand. All except one who, behind his back, had his fingers crossed!

The other incident was a lesson in buffoonery. There was a bracket welded near a place where two corridors met. A foreman measured its distance from the deck; then measured it for a second time. Then, looking around in all directions to make sure he wasn't being observed, he removed his hard hat and smacked his head into the bracket. He walked to the other side and repeated the performance, each time shouting out an expletive. He replaced his safety helmet, made a note on the back of a cigarette packet and, having done so, walked off whistling nonchalantly.

Wha's like us, eh?

A Reasonable Man

(or a fellow worker's position on intolerance)

'You have your Jews, Hindus, Buddhists, Muslims and a' thi' rest – a' doing their ain thing. Fair enough. Live an' let live, ah say – we're a' Jock Tamson's bairns efter a'. They've got their way a' doing things, an' we've got oors. An' who among us can claim to know it a'? We're a' in this big world thigither, so we must a' learn fae each ither an' learn tae be respectful of a' thi different ways o' daein' stuff. But hivin' said that, I think maybe the Catholics' service goes on just a wee bit too long, an' that's how they hiv tae pish up ma close when they come oot.'

The Birthday Cake

Many years back I was employed as a maintenance painter in a bakery, which no longer exists. The firm, by far not the worst that I had ever worked for, demanded loyalty from all their employees as this tale will highlight.

One day a wee angry Maryhill housewife stormed into one of the firm's outlets. She carried, at arm's length, a child's birthday cake. The Manager approached her, noticing her anxious state. He saw at once that embedded in the lurid icing was a fully grown cockroach.

'Ah'm on ma way doon tae thi Health Inspector's office tae show him whit yous are dishin' up. It's a pure disgrace, so it is. An' that wee wean is cryin' her eyes oot – a beastie in her birthday cake!'

In a flash, too fast for the wee woman, the Manager's hand shot out, grabbed the cockroach and swallowed it in one deft movement.

'What beastie are you on about?' he demanded.

'Ya dirty big bastard' the woman quickly responded.

As she stormed out the shop, he shouted after her: 'Wish the wean a happy birthday from me!'

Loyalty like that – you cannot buy it.

The Meeting

The management had offered a penny. A whole penny an hour rise, if we adopted new working practices. The new agreement would mean giving up the few minutes' grace that we traditionally had for clocking on for the morning shift. To some of the better timekeepers it seemed a good offer. Others weren't so sure. And for the habitual latecomers it was an offer too far. But this analysis is an oversimplification of the situation that existed in the paint department of the shipyard. The nearest analogy would be found in some gathering of monks in the dark ages debating about how many angels could dance on the head of a pin. Even this example wouldn't do justice to the men whose brains were addled by a lifetime of breathing in noxious fumes and arguing just for the hell of it.

Anyhow, the proposed deal had arrived and it would have to be addressed. There never is a good time for such things, but it had come at the worst time of year for serious discussion owing to the fact that working on a half-completed ship in winter is unbearable and a meeting in a hut out of the icy wind tends to drag on, as nobody wants to bring the proceedings to a close and return to the frozen ship.

In Glasgow around this time the sun takes a sabbatical. It's dark going to work and dark on the homeward journey. The condition called S.A.D. (seasonally affected disorder) is far too fancy for us tough guys, but we are all fully paid-up sufferers. It's a long stretch too, from the Bacchanalian September weekend to Hogmanay. To face the long dark days wearing damp overalls and hard, uncomfortable, steel toe-capped ill-fitting boots doesn't help either. Wearing your pyjamas under your jeans is only one of the futile attempts at fighting back. The steel is so cold it burns the skin off your hands, should you be so forgetful as to touch it. Enough already. If I describe it any further I'll depress myself too much to write this tale.

What makes shipyard life bearable is one thing and one thing only: the famous gallows humour. It may not be everyone's cup of tea, but these guys were what made up the legendary audience of the Glasgow Empire.

To make those men laugh takes a high degree of wit, humour and skill… and there are purveyors aplenty.

In the yards were famous patter merchants and tellers of tales, who could keep their fellow workers laughing at all times. But these giants were silenced by the penny offer. This deal had set man against man. Lifetime friends no longer spoke to each other. Double acts, like Semmit and Drawers worked solo now. Tea breaks were unbearable with men munching away, their faces buried in their daily newspapers. The usual ribald remarks that accompanied the turning to page three were no longer made. The noise of the munching, like so many cattle in a shed, still fills me with dread. That and the ticking of the time clock were the only sounds that could be heard.

The shop stewards watched these events unfold with trepidation. Daily, the situation grew worse. The powerful unity that had been painstakingly built up over many years of struggle was being eroded at an awesome speed. Something had to be done. It was decided to call a departmental meeting to clear the air once and for all.

As one of the shop stewards (or shop stupids as we were affectionately called (I think it was affectionate)), I shared the apprehension felt by my co-steward about the outcome of the meeting, but there was no alternative. I wasn't interested in the result, but I was in full agreement that we must call an end to our civil war and get back to our previous proud reputation as a reliable department upholding the best traditions of trade unionism.

We had always played a principled part in the complex machinations of shipbuilding and it would be sad indeed if it all came to an end over a penny. The money was insignificant, what with reductions it would amount to less than eight pence per week. Not even enough for a quarter gill, or as one guy put it: 'I've spilt mair doon the front o' ma shirt on a night oot'.

The date for the meeting was agreed on. It would be three weeks hence and to this effect we posted a notice on the board in our hut. I wrote the date in large print, as it would have to compete with all manner of announcements, pin-ups, football scores, thank you notes from beneficiaries of our mutual aid scheme and the usual newspaper cuttings with the obscenities pencilled in.

By announcing that there was to be a debate the tension eased a little and bit by bit the atmosphere returned to something resembling our old ways. Jokes began to be told and banter could be heard as the men thawed and old couplings were renewed; sexual exploits were lyingly told for the first time in ages. It was easier to begin a serious discussion on the issues now that the needle was removed from the equation. It was now even possible to joke about the sectarian divide – always a good barometer on Clydeside.

The old humour gathered momentum until we were back to our unchallenged position as the yard's maddest and funniest department. We were proud of our premier position and worked hard at maintaining it. Even sensible men in our workforce did their bit to keep us in the number one spot. Staid grandmasters of their lodges could be seen indulging in madcap behaviour to hold their end up. Everyone played their part. This is the esprit-de-corps that lies behind such historic victories as the famous UCS Work-in.

Incidentally, a serious study needs to be undertaken on the contribution that Clydeside humour has played in industrial struggles – and why so much of what's depicted in the media on industrial action is so po-faced and dull.

Jackie fished the rubber woman from the river. It was punctured and floated lifeless on top of the water, falling and rising with the slow swell.

It had last seen service aboard a Swedish ore-carrier. Not wishing to be explicit, I'll leave it to the reader to visualise. What that service entailed I'll omit for the sake of your refined sensibilities, but suffice to say that it/she had been serviced to death. After all, these rubber ladies weren't meant to last a lifetime, unlike the real ones; usually one trip being enough, then love died due to rubber having a finite life span. Sometimes though these ore-carriers sailed longer distances than normal to deliver their cargo and this particular dolly looked tired from such a trip.

Her colour had gone. The sea water had seen to that. Her blonde nylon hair had faded for the same reason, but the worst thing was 'she' was covered in tar oil and all the filth from our polluted oceans. You wouldn't have touched 'her' with the proverbial bargepole, but that is exactly what Jackie did. He fished the doll out from a floating mass of detritus, which included a fair number of Clyde Herring (for non-shipbuilders, that's the name we give to used prophylactics).

The mirth Jackie's escapade caused was infectious; the story swept the through the yard being told and retold with relish. He had decided to restore the doll to 'her' previous beauty and to do so he had hidden her in a part of the ship rarely visited by any foremen. He kept the location secret from his workmates, also for obvious reasons. There he cleaned and painted her and gradually brought her back to 'life'. He re-dyed her faded hair, procured a special adhesive and mended the punctures. He patiently waited until the glue had done its work, then the moment of truth. Jackie didn't hesitate; he put his mouth to her valve and blew. Big Jimmy Reid said 'We not only build ships, we build men'. Jackie was such a man. Faced with this task most of us would back away, but not Jackie. He blew until 'she' filled out in all the right places. She lay there with her firm rounded body and freshly painted nipples standing erect. Her arms were raised triumphantly. She lay unblinking, scarlet mouth opened in astonishment. Stories of her restoration kept everyone interested and, in the period leading up to the meeting, served to deflate any remaining tensions (there must be some Freudian pun there).

The meeting lived up to our expectations. It was extremely difficult for us as stewards to explain the case from the management's side and to highlight our position. We were trying to get a vote of acceptance. The arguments raged from all sides of the floor. Sometimes it looked like we were carrying the day, only to see our position swept away by some colourful turn of phrase. It seemed everyone had an opinion on the deal and the debate swung back and forth between acceptance and refusal in equal measure. Speakers used every trick that they had learned in the tough cauldron of Scottish politics. Slanders were high on the agenda, as were put-downs and weak jokes.

Old histories were dragged up that weren't particularly relevant, but it gave the speaker the chance to replay old battles in which they had played a prominent role and, far more importantly, highlighted this or that person who had maybe voted the wrong way. The wrong way that is from the speaker. The next man would invariably be the person who had wrongly voted. He, in his turn, would dredge up his old position and try to win the long forgotten war. And so it dragged on.

The hours ticked by. As the guy chairing the meeting was in his foreman's bad books and was pencilled in for a punishment job, he was in no hurry to bring the proceedings to a halt.

But reality must be faced – like Tam O'Shanter, 'nae man can tether time nor tide' – and I called for the vote to be taken. 'Right brother' I said, 'whatever way the vote goes – that's it! We've all had our say and now it's 'make your mind up time'. It's a simple 'aye' or 'naw', we're no having anyone abstaining – we don't wear that in this team. And, like always, when a decision has been taken, we don't go in the huff if it doesn't go our way. Right sober up now and let's vote in the usual fashion. A straight show of hands – thank you, brothers.'

There was the usual shuffling of heavy boots as the men silently composed themselves.

'All those in favour of the deal, please show' said my co-steward. A forest of waving hands went up. A quick count was taken by two guys from opposing sides of the debate. 'Thirty', one said. The steward now asked for all those opposing to show in the same way. Again a bunch of hands. The same two men counted them. Twenty-eight, twenty-nine, thirty…thirty-one. That was it. The management's proposal was thrown out. The vote had been taken. Our democratic rights had been exercised. The result would stand, like marriage, for better or for worse – it was final. Fait-accompli, over, finito, goodnight Vienna. The air had been cleared. Semmit and Drawers were sharing a roll-up; others, who had not been working near each other, were hugging close and shouting into each other's ears, shipyard-style. Hard hats were picked up and one by one the painters left the hut and made their way back to resume building ships.

I was glad – relaxed even. All the tension was gone. It was a good feeling; it was the best that I had felt for weeks. Only one thing puzzled me: I had always thought that we had only sixty in the department. In the heat of battle I hadn't given the matter my fullest attention. In yards such as ours, there was always men leaving and new starts arriving and I usually kept on top of it. But of late my mind had been full with the offer. It was a puzzle – ach, what did it matter. It had all been resolved. I started tidying up the hut; sweeping out all the cigarette ends and old chewing gum. I had nearly finished the chores when I noticed it.

It stuck out from a pile of dustsheets. It was an inflatable arm raised in salute. Her mouth was opened in astonishment at the outcome of the vote. I tucked her arm back under the sheet and left the hut. I laughed out loud. Shipyard men – they're something else.

The Singer

Glasgow, sometime in the 1950's, and a squad of painters are painting the city's number one hotel. Staying at the hotel is one of America's foremost crooners, who is appearing nightly in Glasgow's famed Empire Theatre to full houses.

To one of the squad it seemed like his golden opportunity and as he jumped around on the scaffolding he sang at the top of his voice the songs made famous by the US star.

He was well-used to singing as he worked and although his voice was pleasant enough, he had learned to maximise it to best effect by using alcoves, window mullions and recesses of whatever building he was painting. His workmates joked about his singing, but only in a light-hearted way, as it always helped to pass the time.

At tea break, they all clambered down and crowded into a side room off the main lobby. They had only just sat down when the hotel commissionaire entered the room and enquired who was the singer among them.

The painter felt a rush of elation. Had he been heard by the star? It was as good an audition as he could ever have dreamed of and it looked like he'd struck gold.

He rose to meet the commissionaire who put his hand into his uniform and announced that he had a letter for him from the star.

The painter's heart was thumping. You read about such things happening to this person or that and how they got taken up and became stars themselves. Donald Pearce of the Babbling Brook was one such person.

With trembling, paint-covered hands he opened the envelope and read:

To the painter singing outside my window. Please could you sing somewhere else. I had a late show last night and you'll understand I need my sleep. Look after yourself, buddy.

It was signed by the star in his own handwriting. At any other time the painter would have valued such a note, but he crumpled it up, threw it away and, sick of heart, returned to join his mates. He finished off his, now cold, tea.

They might even have got on to this trick by now.

THERE WERE THESE THICK PADDIES..........

THIS CARTOON HAS BEEN USED IN MANY NEWSPAPER ARTICLES HIGHLIGHTING THE 'IRISH QUESTION' — IT HAS BEEN FEATURED ON FESTIVAL T-SHIRTS AND ALBUM COVERS* AND CALENDARS ETC. INCIDENTLY I NEVER GOT PAID FOR ANY OF IT.

* THAT PETROL EMOTION BAND

THE STRANGE THING MORAG IS WHY WE HAVE THE DULLEST FOOD IN THE WORLD
HAGGIS
PORRIDGE
STARRETT.

WAR CHEST
PUBLIC PURSE

A LIGHTHEARTED LOOK AT THE 'WHA'S LIKE US' SCHOOL

A BUNCH OF BANKERS AND HEDGE FUND MANAGERS ADDRESS THE ISSUE OF CARING CAPITALISM.

"By laying hands upon the trades unions we have rescued the people from an incalculable amount of internal strife and discord.
We have done away with primitive and senseless methods of settling economic differences"

ADOLF HITLER

STARRETT

STARRETT.
MT

Throw in the towel Prime Minister this one is going the distance.

THERE SEEMS TO BE SOME CONFUSION AS TO WHAT IS MEANT BY THE TERM **WORKING CLASS.** IF THE ABOVE PIECE OF APPARATUS WAKES YOU IN THE MORNING THERE IS NO NEED FOR FURTHER DOUBT — YOU KNOW ALREADY

P.S. – 'SWEATY SOX' THE COLLOQUIAL TERM FOR SCOTSMEN IN USE BY THE WORKING CLASS IN THAMES ESTUARY BRITAIN

It's our best seller at the moment.

WOW! YET ANOTHER RECESSION AND STILL IT TAKES PEOPLE BY SURPRISE — WE'RE SLOW LEARNERS

TONIGHT
CAILY
CEIDHL
CEILDHY
DISCO
SCO
WHI
STARRETT.

THERE'S OUR SHARE
OIL SLICK
STARRETT

MIAOW!

SCOTLAND
CLOSED
AT LAST!

36,000 FAMILIES IN HOUSES THAT HAVE NEITHER BATH OR W.C.
23·8% WITHOUT HOT WATER
NO JOBS FOR SCHOOL LEAVERS
JOBS LOST DURING 'BOOM'
ENGINEERING - 70,000
TEXTILES - 25,000
MANUFACTURING INDUSTRY - 126,000
BRONCHITIS 0·84 DEATHS PER 1,000
T.B. 0·09 DEATHS PER 1,000
GARRETT

THE 'BOOM'

U.C.S. Production up 87% with a reduction in manpower of 25%
Yes John I think that qualifies as a lame-duck.

Now this is one ANGRY BRIGADE We don't want a run in with Mr Davies.

UCS

SC
RESOURCES
TLAND
FINANCIAL
INSTITUTIONS
OF THE
CITY OF LONDON

MULTINATIONAL COMPANIES
DON'T BOTHER TO WRAP IT PAL WE'LL TAKE IT LIKE IT IS

HERE IS THE NEWS — SCOTLAND'S ANNUAL DROUGHT PROBLEM IS WITH US AGAIN!

WORLD DEPRESSION
1974
NOT IN THE SOCIALIST PART OLD`UN
1975
STARRETT.

BELIEVE ME LADDIE STAY IN IT GETS BETTER

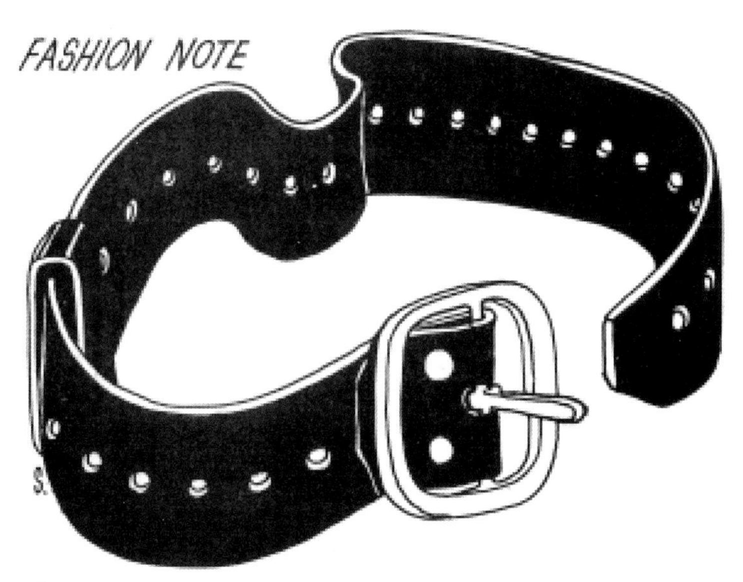

THE BELT THAT HAS BEEN DESIGNED FOR US BY THE MULTI – NATIONAL COMPANIES

DON'T LET HIM HEAR YOU SAY POLITICS AND POETRY DON'T MIX

MY MOTHER THINKS I'M HELPING OLD LADIES ACROSS THE ROAD

STARRITT.
THESE ARE MY MOUNTAINS ..... I THINK?

CAPITALISM CAN'T LET GLASGOW FLOURISH
PAIN

"I could maybe get you a job as a programme seller at the Glasgow Olympics"

FIGHT UNEMPLOYMENT AND THE CUTS!

Wilson's Legacy!

YOU JUST CAN'T BEAT THE OLD 'FREE SPEECH' PLOY

FISH RESTAURANT
CHIPS - 18p.
FISH SUPPER - 43p.
BARCLAYCARD
welcome here
Access
EUROCARD
Cardholders welcome
Fish Restaurant

ART FOR ART'S SAKE
GROWL
GROWL!
KICK
STARRETT.

ALL ART ABOVE
A CERTAIN LEVEL
OF MEDIOCRITY IS
ALWAYS AN ART

OF PROTEST
CRITICISM
& REVOLT

ERNST
FICSHER

HEAR!
HEAR!

"AYE!" "IF IT WAS RENTS OR PRICES IT WOULD RISE A LOT FASTER!"

"YE'LL ALWAYS FIND A WELCOME IN DEAR AULD GLASGOW TOON"
SCOTLAND AGAINST APARTHEID
BOYCOTT
BOYCOTT SOUTH AFRICA
END INVESTMENT
S.T.U.C. AGAINST APARTHEID
SOUTH AFRICA
ANTI-APARTHEID MOVEMENT SCOTLAND
END S. AFRICAN INVESTMENT

art as a weapon

Cartons & Lino Prints by Bob Starrett and Brian McGeoch. Sponsored by the STUC and exhibited at various labour movement events. Available free of charge to labour movement organisations — contact Scottish Marxist.

CROSSROADS ?

DON'T GET CAUGHT WITH THE FILTH

STARRETT.
THE THING I'D HATE MOST ABOUT COMMUNISM IS THAT YOU'D LOSE YOUR INDIVIDUALITY

IF, AND IF EVER, SCOTLAND GAINS ITS INDEPENDENCE THE DEBATE WILL THEN BE OPENED UP AS TO WHAT KIND OF SOCIETY WILL BE ON OFFER. I WELCOME THE SCOTTISH NATION HANDLING ITS OWN AFFAIRS AS IT WILL TAKE ANY ANTI-ENGLISH FEELING OUT OF THE EQUATION AND FORCE TO THE FOREFRONT ANY CONTRADICTIONS THAT EXIST IN OUR COUNTRY AND MAY EVEN MAKE US UNDERSTAND OUR TRUE HISTORY AND STOP VEIWING EVERYTHING THROUGH THE TARTAN SPECTACLES.

The White Christmas

It was Christmas week. The week the management usually tried it on. They had engineered a dispute over a minor matter, possibly a dummy run to test our militancy for the forthcoming pay negotiations. To us in the paint department it came as no surprise, but so near the festivities it was something we could have done without. People outwith the shipbuilding industry in no way could have understood the banality of the 'high heid-yins'.

The painters reluctantly called for strike action – strike while the iron is hot, etc. – but when the department walked out of the yard there was no rejoicing. The stewards had carried the day. No easy task with the department composed of: owner-occupiers; guys behind with the rent; those who had booked the hotel in Magaluf; the malcontent 'Agin' Section'; and the majority who just wanted to work for a fair reward.

Out of the yard I walked in silence with my mate Willie. We had argued for industrial action and had won the debate.

Won? We were days away from Christmas and we were skint. Presents, the Ne'erday drink and the January deluge of bills – it was overwhelming in its consequences.

Willie was Willie, though. What can I say? He would be the guy in the prison camp that can purloin all kinds of escape materials from the guards. He'd dig the tunnel as well.

We, if we've been lucky, have met the Willies – I was lucky. We had mated up years back and made a good team.

Willie spoke at last, 'There might be something that could save the day.'

'Go on' I said

'There is a factory that's shutting down for a week for a paint job. A wee bird told me that the factory inspectors have insisted that it gets painted immediately or they will take action and close the place for keeps.'

'Sounds serious, Willie. Where do we fit in?'

'The owner is looking for a five-man squad to blitz it – and they need to start tonight. I'm thinking we could take it on ourselves. What do you think?'

'Five men, eh? I don't know. Is it a big place?'

'You'll know tonight, wee man. I phoned him and agreed to do it last night, but I had to wait on the outcome of the meeting.'

What if the vote had gone against you?'

'Well, it would be a no-show.'

'And how did you know I'd be up for it?'

'Because, like me, you're in the grubber.'

I shook my head and laughed for the first time that day. Then, agreeing to meet him later, I jumped a bus for home.

We met up late that evening. It was a cold, damp, west of Scotland night and we shivered as we made our way to an industrial area; enviously looking in at brightly-lit houses, as we headed away from the built-up, populated district to our grim destination.

We carried brushes and rollers – nothing fancy. This was to be what we in the trade called 'a hit'. No sheets would be needed. We would pour the paint on the floor and charge our rollers in what, in effect, was a puddle of material. Working at speed it wouldn't be there long. Decorating it was not.

We picked up the keys from a security man and let ourselves in to the factory. Willie switched on the lights and we both gasped simultaneously. The place was HUGE!

'We can't possibly finish this in time.'

'Well, if we don't we get hee-haw. That's the deal.'

'It would be a hard shift for the five men, never mind us, Willie.'

'Where's your spirit of adventure, wee man? It's a gamble. A challenge. Do or die. If we don't do it in time the place is shut and we're still in the grubber, but knackered as well.'

'Sounds great.'

‘Shut up and let’s strike a blow for freedom!’

‘You missed your vocation. You should have entered politics.’

We made a start by moving at least a hundred of the thousands of cardboard boxes that filled the place. We were soon sweating with the effort, although our breath could be seen clearly in the vast factory. We opened the drums of paint stacked there and made our first ‘puddle’. No time for chat; we were off. Game on.

After a few hours had passed, Willie went off and found the kitchen. He brewed up a mug of tea for himself and one of soup for me. Hunting through the kitchen cupboards, he found a portion of Christmas cake and even a cracker, which we pulled. It never made a sound; just limply tore open and I claimed the paper hat. We stood, rather than sit at the table. From past experience, we knew this to be fatal; if you sit down, you can’t get back up again.

Having eaten the cake we returned to our task, me now wearing my paper crown. Willie looked at the enormous area that lay in front of us.

‘We should have brought a magic wand with us. This is some fight we’ve got ourselves into’ I sighed.

We now had to climb up to the girders, carrying two extremely heavy planks. Once we had positioned the scaffold boards we descended to collect the paint. We stripped to our underwear under our disposable overalls, covered our faces in Vaseline and made the first brushstroke.

‘The longest journey starts with the first step’ I declared.

‘Shut up and keep painting’ was the curt response.

The trick to painting large areas is not to concentrate too much and you MUST NEVER EVER count the brushstrokes – that way lies madness.

Hour followed hour. On and on went our task. We were now into a rhythm and worked with and around each other, without having to debate the how or why or where to apply the paint. We were like an old married couple.

We planned to complete a bay within a certain time and repeat the operation *ad nauseam*.

In no time at all we were covered from head to foot in the dust that covered the girders.

Here, I'll take the opportunity to describe how to move from one bay to another without the time-consuming need to descend – painters can skip this part!

The manoeuvre is known as 'frogging' and consists of launching one plank from the other. The operative kneels on one of the planks and makes his way to the end of it, all the time pushing the second plank ahead of him. When more of the second plank overhangs the bottom one the operative summons all his strength and fires the board towards the next girder. If he has timed his act to perfection the plank will land on the girder. He will have to regain his balance on completion of this tricky act. And all done without the aid of a safety net, quite awe-inspiring!

When we had made a fair attack on the job we decided on a short break to stretch our legs and attend to a much needed toilet visit. We used the occasion to tidy ourselves, as we now resembled snowmen, but with dirty snow. We spent a bit of time clearing our throats and noses; making all sorts of animal noises as we did so. After gulping down water and covering our faces in Vaseline again, we resumed our work; spitting ferociously as we went. No glamour here.

By this time it was daylight, but we ignored the fact. We were not going to be sidetracked by anything that smacked of normality. So it came and went until it was, again, night. We worked on trancelike. Now our bodies operated automatically, on and on, brushstroke after brushstroke. Then, after a certain quota of bays had been completed, we came down to floor level and began rolling the walls, each man dreaming his own dreams.

Periodically, Willie would throw a lump of Vaseline and dust to attract my attention to a section missed or some other banal reason.

We ached in all our joints. Our bodies screamed out for rest, the luxury of which could only be experienced in our delirium.

At any given time, one or other of us would need to be brought out of the dream-time. There were also the periods when we spoke in tongues, like some Southern Baptist mission hall.

Willie attempted to explain something, but being so choked with dust was unable to. I, in trying to respond, was equally hopeless. We needed to take stock, so Willie indicated he was heading to the kitchen to brew up and would give me a shout in a few minutes. All this he communicated by signs and mime, but being shipyard workers, used to working in a cacophony of screeching sound, it was all so normal.

I worked on in a kind of stupor; time had no meaning; life outside of this factory had ceased to exist. 'I must sleep' I thought or I'll die. I don't know how it happened, but I slumped into one of the cardboard boxes and instantly was asleep.

I was abruptly wakened by a ghostly apparition – Santa Claus! Santa Claus? Help me! I've gone insane! It came towards me. Oh, the terror. And I don't believe in him…

'You should see your face, man' Willie roared with laughter as removed the white beard. He had found the outfit in the cupboard next to where he'd found the Christmas cake; remains of the works do before the shut down.

'Fair's fair, wee man, it's my turn' Santa said, as he lay down on top of his scarlet cloak. He began snoring at once. I've always loved the sound of snoring, ever since I was a child and saw the dwarfs in the film Snow White sleeping peacefully.

I concentrated my thoughts on how I would tell this story when next in the company of painters and we were swapping 'war stories'.

'Snore on, Willie, my man.' I imagined I could even see the line of ZZZzzzz's that cartoonists use to depict sleep.

Eventually, I had to wake him so that we could attempt to rally ourselves and somehow complete the job. We walked to where we had applied our first brushstroke all that time ago. What was it? Days? It was certainly many, many hours.

On seeing that we only had a couple of bays to go, our adrenaline kicked in and we regressed into our childhood. We tumbled boxes over, kicked dust at one another and applied paint to ourselves in a childish game of 'last to touch'.

Then, rejuvenated, we raced through the final section and at last the job was done.

We were getting ourselves cleaned up when the owner arrived. He inspected the work and, well pleased, called us over to the kitchen table.

'Well done, lads! Splendid work. That gets those bastards off my back. They gave me that daft ultimatum; closing the place down and all that toffee. I'll be honest with you; I found it hard to get any painters to do the work. I mean, what's a bit of asbestos, eh? All those boxes are full of brake linings, for Chrissakes. We all – you, me – use the material. Am I right? Course I am. And, anyhow, what's a bit of dust?'

We looked at each other. For days we had been covered in the stuff. We had breathed it in hourly. We made a face at each other.

The owner peeled off our pay from a roll in his coat pocket. Then he peeled off a bundle more.

'That'll get you a Christmas drink, boys. Thanks again. Grand job.' The he left.

Years later Willie and I met up and as we retold the story to each other we were reduced to tears of laughter. We were helpless with laughter – passers-by smiled with joy at the spectacle. It was a sure-fire winner of a tale and we relived that job. It only needed me to say 'Santa Claus' and we would be off again.

I was still laughing as I left Willie and waved to him as he stood at the window of the hospice.

In memory of Willie Bruce, a Govan man.

Paddy at the Barras

Paddy the Irish tinker/strongman/escapologist performing all those years ago on the streets of Glasgow's Barras was surveying his audience, before swallowing a six-foot length of chain that lay on the street.

The tinker eyed the length of chain lying in the Glasgow road.

'I'm going to swallow that' he said, 'but before I do this Paddy is going to share a piece of wisdom with you all. Cleverer men than me say money can buy you anything. I say, no, it can't. And I'll give you three examples to back up my claim.'

He walked round the expectant crowd never taking his eyes off the chain.

He now proclaimed:

'One – you can't buy muscles. Two – you can't buy true love. Three – you can't buy the truth'

He then picked up the chain and, in a series of gulps, swallowed it, leaving a section hanging from the side of his mouth. The crowd, pleased, put money in his hat and left. My old man paid half-a-crown – for the wisest gift of knowledge I've still never heard bettered.

The Paperhangers

The family of house-painters, father and his three sons, were sitting in front of the television. They had had a hard day at the trade and now were relaxing with a beer.

It was a summer evening and in the block across from them a couple could be seen attempting to paper their flat.

'Will you look at the state of them?' said the father as he opened another can of beer. The sons laughed in unison.

The game was about to kick-off, so they made themselves comfortable. Periodically, during the match, this or that son would look over and comment on the progress that the couple were making hanging the paper. Now and then they could hear the man swear as the wallpaper tore, or the wife cry out when the paste went all over the room.

'Look at them' said the father. 'He's trying to match an alternate pattern without having measured the paper.'

'Shoosh, Da! I'm trying to concentrate on the game'.

'Me an' a'' said another son.

They watched the game intently, but with sly glances out the window.

'The first length just fell aff' laughed the youngest son.

'Will you shut up and watch the game' someone said.

'Oh no, he's only hung that length upside down' said another.

It was the sight of the woman bursting into tears and less than five minutes to go until half-time that made the father get up from his chair.

'I can't stand this another minute. It's spoiling the game for me. I'm going over there.' He picked up his jacket.

'Wait for me' cried his oldest son.

'An me' offered the youngest.

'Okay, let's get it done so we can watch the second half in peace' said the remaining son.

Anyone watching that summer's evening would have been cheered up by the sight of four painters papering a room and a wife drying her tears and all this being done in the space of the half-time. When they finished and returned to their places in front of the television, the father explained: 'Ah couldnae relax wi' that performance going on. Ah just had tae get involved.'

'Us tae, Da' responded the sons in unison.

Over the road, two happy people could also relax and also watch the game.

'Ah widnae hae tipped that crowd ower there giein' us a turn – it jist shows ye, eh?' the woman declared.

Clash of Culture, or what?

The Irish landlady was showing the two building workers around her Bayswater house.

'I don't normally take in you Scotties, but you look OK to me. I prefer Irish boys – only normal isn't it. After all, you know what your own are about.'

'My Granny is frae Donegal' said one of the two. 'Does that count?'

She looked at him with a grim expression.

'No drinking indoors, mind. This is a good Catholic home. I know some of you lads like to bring in a drink and I just won't have it. No dolly birds either, mind'

'You don't need to worry on that score' instantly replied the other building worker. 'We can't even get a kind look frae they London lassies.'

She opened the door to the bedroom and instantly they were face-to-face with a large picture of the Virgin Mary. One of the workers leapt back in horror, caught unexpectedly.

She glared at him. 'Our Lady gave you a start, Jocky boy? Maybe she knows something about you that I don't, but I'm warning you – anything out of the ordinary and you're out.'

They viewed the twin beds. Both had large crucifixes attached to the headboards. On the table between the beds were a stack of religious tracts and a ceramic holy statue. The statue was chipped in a number of places indicating serious wear and tear. On every wall there were pictures, large and small, of the Madonna.

She saw them looking. 'Oh, yes, boys. She is with me every day.'

They put their small suitcases down, tossed a coin to determine who got what bed. When that was out of the road, they unpacked their tools, carefully checking that they were in pristine order. They were on their way to earning some of that Big Money that everyone told stories about in the pubs back home in Glasgow. Later on, as they went downstairs to go out and begin the search for the sites that would pay that Big Money, they were called in to the kitchen.

It was mayhem. There were children of all ages squabbling round the kitchen table. The noise was something to behold.

She shouted above the din 'They're all my little treasures, thanks be to God, each and every one of them.'

She broke off for the merest second to cuff one around the ears. 'Leave Dermot alone, Liam!'

'But Mammy…' His appeal was lost in the overwhelming noise.

The two builders handed over the money for the lodgings and left.

Day after day they passed the kitchen on their way to work. She would wave if she was able, but often she never heard them leave, as the children were being too rowdy. Too rowdy for any normal scale of measurement, but not for the landlady.

Day after day she would interrupt their privacy by entering their room without knocking to bring them the latest tracts that the Church had given her.

She often enquired about what the boys prayed for.

'Oh, just the usual, er, world peace, an' that' replied the youngest of the two builders.

'Well, just remember, she can hear your every word and see your very thoughts' as she said this she pointed at the largest holy picture.

It had all got too much for one of the builders and he snapped:

'Why didn't you take a leaf out of her book, you know, and remain a virgin. I don't know what you're thinking about with that rabble, but if you think you're doing a service to your Church by increasing their numbers, well, it's not on. You're no' like the Virgin Mary, more like the old woman who lived in the shoe!'

We were looking for new digs that afternoon. Oh, and we never did find the sites that paid the Big Money.

Had Brush and Did Travel

A few decades back I was in Switzerland as a *gastarbeiter*, translated that means guestworker. I'm not too sure about the guest part, but I was certainly a worker and in that capacity I was to be exploited unmercifully without recourse to withdrawing my labour, strikes being illegal.

I was employed by a father and son combination - a small painting outfit in the land of the cuckoo clock – and I was along with other poor sods helping to keep society functioning. The indigenous young men preferring to work in one of the many international financial set-ups.

The work was hard and executed at top speed, as only the fastest remained employed. Each week all over the country could be seen young foreigners leaving who had failed to keep up with the tempo.

There is an old story told down the years by housepainters. The boss's son working alongside other apprentices suggests that they race to see who can paint the fastest. Well you get the point.

This day I had been paired with a young tearaway from Liverpool who will remain nameless in case he reads this piece. Anyhow his knowledge of our new land was limited to what he read in the 'Victory' and 'Commando' comics and mine wasn't that good either. I knew a guy had shot an apple off his son's head and somehow a piece of music celebrating this event was used for the 'Lone Ranger IV' series.

We were based in Grubunden which is a German speaking region and consequently that was the language our boss addressed us in when we lined up before him in the mornings. As we stood on the snow we all hoped that we would be sent to some kind of indoor work because it was cold. Yes, I know you're thinking: 'But it's a dry cold'. Climb out from under your duvet at 5.30am, put on your cold working clothes and make your way through the dark to the workshop looking up at the window where other people still seemed asleep and tell me that.

Me and the Liverpool guy were instructed to put our tools in the boss's car. He then told the other painters that as there was nothing for them go away and come back the following week. This was meekly accepted by the disappointed workforce. What else could they do?

It was indicative that work was scarce and this was highlighted when the son joined us in the car. He volunteered to drive.

We set off and headed away from the town towards the mountains. The day was getting lighter and the place looked stunning. Holidaymakers see a different country always and I felt a bit like one of them as we were driven over sparkling iced roads.

Father and son conversed as we travelled: 'Achtung. Kaput. Raus, Raus'. No, not really but to our hearing it sounded like the banal war films we had seen.

Now we were driving up the steep mountain road at what I felt was too fast a speed. He was a good driver, I'll give him that, and he controlled the car with great skill as we skidded near to the road's edge at every bend. It was, by now, daylight, so we could look down at the sheer drop that would be ours should he lose his concentration. The Liverpool man was car sick. I always had assumed that was one of these 'fake' illnesses the middle-class imagined they suffered from, like migraines and Stendhal syndrome (for those who aren't yet acquainted with this affliction it's what happens when you attempt to experience all the beauty of Florence in one sitting. A nauseous turn brought on by the sheer wonder of it all). Since he was from Liverpool this could be ruled out. As for 'car sickness' I had hardly spent too much time in a car myself and then I had enjoyed the experience so much I vowed I would join the ranks of car owners, at the earliest opportunity.

Anyhow, car sick it was and he became more and more agitated the further we climbed. Our ears popped and the air was so cold it nipped the inside of our noses and even made me feel lightheaded.

We sat at the back discussing our wages and conditions getting angrier by the mile – oops! kilometre.

We were now descending and were on a very treacherous stretch of road. I could tell this from the tone of apprehension in the son's voice. Father barked out commands in a stressful manner.

The Liverpool man was taking no part in anything now. Sitting back in the seat he was what could only be termed aggressive smoking. He took short drags through clenched teeth. His eyes narrowed as he exhaled. He nudged me:

'What are these geezers on about?', he wanted to know.

I thought I would add a bit of levity into the journey, 'Ach, they're only going on about how they want you to work harder.'

'What?' he replied. 'Work harder? Who do this crowd think they are?'

He continued muttering between draws on his cigarette periodically asking me what they were saying.

He knew me well enough to know I didn't understand the language but in his hyper state must have forgotten.

'What's he saying now?' he nodded in the direction of Paul.

'Just something about how he doesn't like anyone to smoke in the car.'

I had no sooner finished the sentence than the Liverpool man sat forward in the seat and stubbed his cigarette in to the neck of the son. His hands left the wheel in pain. The car was out of control sliding all over the road and as he had his foot jammed hard on the accelerator we were still going fast. We smashed into the inside of the road towards the edge and the sheer drop. I was terrified. The father tried to grab the steering wheel but was thrown back in his seat banging his head at the same time. He howled '*Fertig, kaput*' which I know from the aforementioned 'Commando' comic means 'all is finished' and I honestly believed the same thing. Eventually the vehicle impaled itself on the metal roadside barrier and stopped. Shaken we all clambered out. The Malermeister was screaming. By the way he spat and pointed I knew we were 'fired'. No translation was necessary. The Liverpool friend was shouting too 'We won the war you bastards and don't you ever forget it'.

'But they're Swiss!' I attempted to explain.

The moral?...There isn't one!

The Milk Carton

The squad all worked together in harmony, and why not, they had been doing the same tasks in unison, give or take a different ship or two, for years.

Kelly straightened up from scraping old paint from the ship's deck. It was hard, thirsty work and a drink was required. He searched, in vain, in his overall pocket. He required a 5p coin for the milk machine. Dunky, a co-worker, observing his plight produced two 5ps.

'Get me a carton when you go...thanks mate'.

Kelly took the money and set off. Dunky worked away as before but with the anticipation of quenching his thirst with a cold carton of milk. Kelly eventually returned holding one carton. Dunky reached out to receive it, only to be informed by Kelly that he had put both coins in the milk machine but Dunky had lost his.

With that he opened the carton and proceeded to drink.

The Worried Men

The delegates from the Clyde were in 10 Downing Street taking part in discussions with Edward Heath about the need to save the jobs in the shipbuilding industry. They were the representatives of the workers who were engaged in a 'work-in' at Upper Clyde Shipbuilders. After lengthy argument the Prime Minister shook his head and attempted to explain how difficult it was to run a country.

'Do you know the worries I have?' said Heath.

William 'Bugsy' McGuiness retorted: 'Worries? – You think *you've* got worries? – I support Partick Thistle!'

All Life Is Here

Work, bad behaviour, kindness, drama and greed – all in a short period.

He was painting the side of the vessel – the trade called it the shell. He had staked his claim to the job and was so conscientious and possessive of the task that he exercised territorial rights of sorts and called it 'Ma shell'. From that it was a short step to the team nicknaming him 'Michelle', and on occasion to annoy him they would sing a line or two of the Beatles' classic.

One day while he worked away he fell from the raft into Clyde, which at that time was in spate. He churned up the brown water in desperation, but it was hopeless on three counts. One, his life jacket was lying on the raft. He had removed it, as he habitually did to facilitate using the long pole of the roller. The second was that he was wearing heavy layers of clothing to keep out the freezing wind, which were now waterlogged. Third, the steel toe-capped industrial boots.

He was being swept, at speed, along the side of the ship and some young guys, not understanding the very real tragedy that was developing, were shouting banal utterances at him as he passed: 'Where's yer pieces?', 'Did ye take yer Record wi' ye?'. The worst thing was a young worker bending down pretending to take off his boots prior to diving in. 'Fuck me, today of a' days, a double knot'.

Brutal conditions ferment brutal thoughts, sadly.

Michelle vanished beneath the surface, caught by some fierce undercurrent. His bloated body was found three weeks later in a bunch of driftwood and old plastic. How undignified is the exit of men at times.

But on the day of the accident the yard came to a halt and everyone left for home.

The shop stewards were into action at once organising an uplift for his widow. All gave generously, even the crass young guys, perhaps guilt played on their minds.

When the money was counted out in the stewards' office it came to a substantial sum. A steward was delegated to take the cheque to the widow and he set off.

He knocked at the door in Partick and while waiting for the woman to arrive he composed himself. He had never had to undertake such a task as this and he steeled himself.

She opened the door after enquiring who was there.

On being handed the cheque she showed genuine surprise.

'Doesn't look very sad', thought the steward, but you don't know how shock will manifest itself.

She spoke: 'Oh aye him, we've no' been thigither for aboot twenty years. He's staying' wi' some woman up the Drum so they tell me. But thanks a' thi same son, this money will come in handy'.

With that she shut the door in the steward's befuddled face and that brings to an end this sad tale.

The Two Take-Ons

Years ago, with the vanity of youth, I thought I was a bit 'tasty' in the tough guy stakes. I was working on a high-rise tower block with other 'tasty' guys, all except the twins, a frail pair who kept to themselves and conversed as they worked in a low, mumbling fashion. Their most distinguishing feature was that both had a permanent drip from their noses. We 'tough guys' hardly noticed them at all, and when we did it was to discuss something to do with the job or other formalities.

To state that we were all tasty is not strictly true – we told each other we were, but, in fact, we were all in fear of the ganger. This big man was in a different league altogether. He didn't have to act tough – he just was. He bullied the entire workforce. Captain Bligh would have run errands for this guy. He bullied each and every one of us verbally and physically. It had reached the stage that when he passed we waited for a crack to the head and even when it wasn't forthcoming the expectation caused a bit of anxiety.

He had arrived from some out of town place and being none too bright had fought his way up to his present position. Knowing the next stage up was out of his reach, involving as it would writing out timesheets, he had to maintain his status to avoid slipping back into the hoi polloi. Some had challenged him during the early stages of construction and he had thrashed them soundly. He was hard, no question about it.

During the tea breaks the subject of his demise was debated endlessly. It always followed the same lines. What so and so would do if only he didn't have his mortgage to pay. The HP payment. The wife, the kids, the Christmas club. The promise never to use violence that he had given to his dying mother.

The excuses were many, varied and colourful. Perm any one from a hundred. The old fable of the mice and the cat comes to mind. For the punters who haven't had time to read old fables, this is how it goes:

Once long, long ago the mice on board a ship were desperately wanting to eat the big round of cheese stored in the ship's galley. The only difficulty was it was guarded by a large fearsome cat. The mice hold a meeting and some bright mouse comes up with the plan to tie a bell round the cat's neck, that way whenever they hear it ring they can scamper away to safety out of the cat's reach. The mice all agree it's a wonderful idea but one wee mouse speaks up, 'Who is going to bell the cat?' The dream collapses in an instant, end of fable.

That summed up our position exactly, and over the period that the building rose from street level 'til it soared into the sky we 'tough guys' suffered humiliation and humiliation. The majority of us were just like me and it really rankled that this big country boy had our cards so well and truly marked.

This day he thumped one of the twins as he passed. I never found out why, but the other twin looked up from whatever task he was engaged in and with an expressionless face noted the incident.

The ganger entered the hoist that took him to his base in the courtyard on the ground floor.

The twins mumbled to each other and opened a window. They dropped a bucket of scaffolding fittings on top of the ganger and brained him. They closed the window and returned to their work. We tough guys all said that the ganger had it coming to him and the twins had just beaten us to it. Well maybe, but at least one tough guy looked at the frail twins in a more respectful way, nose drips or not.

A Housepainter Remembers His Swinging London

The outlook seemed a lot brighter for young housepainter as he read the letter he had just received from his nativc Glasgow. He was, like many before him, trying to 'make it', as it's called in London. He had arrived in the Big Smoke a few months before, and his confidence and youthful optimism was by now a bit tattered and shopsoiled. London was just too big for him and he knew it.

The papers were full of the Swinging London thing. Lord Do-Nothing was opening a disco somewhere and Lady Do-Nothing was modelling short skirts for some jumped-up Cockney with a camera. It was all 'happening' the newspaper said. If it was, it wasn't happening to him, so he had written to his mates suggesting that they join him. The old strength in numbers story. He painted a rosy picture and as his mates read the same papers, they couldn't get south quick enough to get their share and so they had written confirming that they would be arriving soon.

He looked again and again at the scribble across the sheet of paper to make doubly sure that his eyes weren't tricking him. It was true alright – his mates were coming to join him. He couldn't relax for a second. He was too busy daydreaming about what it would be like with his fellow Glaswegians. He wouldn't be so provincial now. One of the gang had been away from home hundreds of times before, a bit of a tearaway. He was a gifted patter merchant and could get all kinds of birds with his persuasive tongue, it was said. He put the letter carefully on the bedside table to re-read the later, in case he had missed something the previous twenty times. 'Look out London!' he nearly said out loud, as he switched off the light.

In the morning he went as always to the nearby cafe and got his usual slice of toast and mug of tea. It was by no means part of the swinging London scene, and wasn't the cleanest place in the world either, but he felt he could hide away in the drabness of the place. He could relax here among the rest of the customers who in the main were like him, in rooming houses and kept themselves very much to themselves. He soon discovered the reason for the large sale of newspapers in the Capital. It wasn't primarily for reading, but for something to be propped up in front of the silent eaters to tell others to keep their distance. He always sat at the same table – the furthest away from the neon strip, above the serving counter and ate in silence, pretending to read the advertisements surrounding him. He read them every day and knew them word perfect. 'Things go better with...'.

He was interrupted by the girl who worked there speaking to him. He waved her to take the seat facing him, guessing correctly that was what she had said to him. He was thrown out of his stride and had difficulty in communicating at first. But the girl had long since lost count of the customers she had seen in her time like him. She knew his story by heart. Another northerner seduced by the myths of the media. He looked at her pale smiling face that hadn't seen too much sunshine and at the dark greenish, black rings under her eyes where the brutal neon strip cast its shadows. Her most outstanding feature was her superb Roman nose – hooked, yes – but not entirely ugly. She was friendly and indicated by a sign that she wasn't hungry and promptly put her slices of toast in front of him.

He mumbled his thanks and proceeded to dispose of the toast quickly. He was painting on the nearby building site and had a formidable appetite. She repeated the gesture every morning and he began to feel more optimistic. She fancied him – that was clear – but he wasn't in a position to show his feelings. Not yet anyway. Maybe when the rest of the boys got here and some of their confidence rubbed off on him, he'd be in better form. But not now. So he never let his feelings be known to the girl. He though of her giving him the toast and how it would impress his mates. Aye, even Billy, who had been around himself.

More and more he thought of her during the days he painted and he was amazed to find her large nose was getting smaller daily. He was no stranger to the saying that love is blind, but having never been in that condition, and not knowing he was in it now, he didn't want to think too hard about his position. But one thing was certain – he liked her more than he'd admit to anyone.

Only a few days more and the rest of the team would be here. He was looking forward to taking them into the cafe and having them witness the performance with the tea and toast. That would show them. If he could make contact with a real Londoner, and a girl at that, all by himself, what could they accomplish together? Another thing played on his mind. He hoped that they would find her attractive without the toast being considered in the valuation.

At last they were here. All night they spoke of Glasgow and what a dump it was, as if to convince themselves that there was no going back. They asked him a thousand and one questions and he loved the role he was cast in. The queries about work he answered easily enough. The ones about the Kings Road and Carnaby Street, he replied as he did with others about where the 'scene' was. When they asked the inevitable about the birds, he could truthfully say that he had got himself fixed up, and enjoyed the thought. In the morning, when they were all hungry and he was asked did he know of anywhere to eat, he couldn't hide his excitement. He was secretly delighted, as he proudly led the way into his second home and was looking forward to ordering and showing how well he got on with the waitress. Billy especially would be impressed by this, being a great one for chatting up girls in bars and cafes, and showing off his wit.

The girl approached the table with her order notebook in hand. Billy was up in an instant. Out to make a show.

''Ello, alright', he said, the Glaswegian's imitation cockney. 'Bring up five cups of teas and a load of toast luv'.

She smiled at the group and the young housepainter was bursting with pride that Billy was flirting with his girlfriend. He would have liked to have broken the news to them then, but he thought it would be better when they finished their tea. The waitress was still smiling, maybe waiting for the painter to mention their relationship, when Billy said it. In a hard Glaswegian delivery, he said:-

'Where are yer wings dear?'

She replied, 'Why, do you think I'm an angel?'

'Naw, I do nut!' he retorted. 'Ah just couldnae see them giein' ye a beak like that, and no' giein' ye the wings tae go wi' it!'

The girl was mortified and near to tears. The boys roared in approval. This was Billy at his best. Nothing could stop them now. London would be theirs. Only one of the group didn't join in the laughter – he felt sick inside. It was so obscenely cruel. The Scots boys all swaggered out of the cafe with their new found confidence. If they all struck together and had wisecracks like this, they could be unbeatable.

None of them looked back at the girl in the cafe doorway, but one wished he could find the courage to do so. To his shame, he didn't, and he followed the rest along the road with a heavy heart.

If this was the only way to 'make it', then he couldn't care less.

Bobby Goes to Hollywood

(A Jock's adventure in Tinseltown)

Last year I picked up an Oscar. I didn't win one. But I picked up an Oscar. To describe how this came about requires a bit of name-dropping – so if this is not your thing – read no further. Even for the name-dropping fraternity it could be an over rich confection.

But then certain happenings require that a few names be mentioned. Who amongst us could embark on a tale of the Lisbon Lions of '67 without reeling off – McNeil, Lennox, Gemmell... well you get the point. It's Oscar night in Hollywood and I'm right in the thick of the action. What is a wee Maryhill man doing in tinsel town?

Well Lindy Hemming, costume designer, (first name drop) my partner and better half is an Oscar nominee. Better half? Lindy is a qualified nurse who graduated as a stage manager at R.A.D.A., moved to costume designing and after working in the national theatre on many top flight productions, including one that got her nominated for a Tony award on Broadway, transferred to the film industry. My half? I'm good at undercoating. She has been nominated for designing the costumes for Mike Leigh's 'Topsy Turvy', and I'm hanging on to her coat tails. She has worked with Mike since their first collaboration on 'Abigail's Party' and she has brought over all the designers from the film.

We are billeted in Hollywood's Four Seasons Hotel, and on arrival in our suite the first thing we see is an avant-garde brown and white sculpture depicting a can from which rolls of film are spewing out in all directions. Only later when it had melted into a brown puddle did we realise it was chocolate. Innocents abroad right enough.

A knock at the door. A delivery of a couple of 'goody bags' containing designer sunspecs, candied fruits, CDs, a variety of sweets, trinkets; and in my bag, hair straighteners (if only I could use them). These were only the first of many 'goody' bags that we were to receive over the next few days.

The Oscar ceremony was to take place later in the day, but the first part of the proceedings was a 'do' hosted by the British consulate to welcome nominees and partners on behalf of H.M. Government and the British Film Industry.

I stood beside one of the 'Monkees'...y'know the one.

We picked up our goody bags and returned to the hotel to prepare for the main event.

I digress here, not just to drop a few names but to mention something that I'll return to later. Earlier in the year I worked in Edinburgh on a film made by Elton John's Rocket company. The producer was Elton's partner David Furnish, and the movie was called 'Women Talk Dirty' with Gina McKee, Helena Bonham-Carter and Richard Wilson. While in Auld Reekie I had myself kitted out in Scottish evening wear – a Bonnie Prince Charlie Bun Freezer with Pewter Buttons and trews of the Robertson Tartan. I have no clan affiliations, but I used to eat their jam. I only bought the outfit with a view to getting a response at some black tie event in London. Pearly Kings watch out.

Lindy, as a nominee, was being pampered rotten...facials, massages, hair, manicure, a kamikaze couldn't have got treated better – but then they weren't meeting the world's press. I just watched the clock, periodically opening the door to take delivery of yet another goody bag. I took my time dressing in the shortbread tin outfit and preened at myself in the mirror. Coming from the 'proddy, clean and tidy is efficient' school this was something else. 'Aye wee man you look the Jinkies'. Feeling brand new I said to myself 'You shall go to the ball'.

Then it was the obligatory limo and off we set at a funereal pace owing to the fact that the limo was only one of a convoy that stretched for miles. We moved slowly through the placard holding spectators 'Abortion Kills', 'Meat is Murder', 'The third world starves while you pigs go to trough'. I'll defend anyone the right to demonstrate, but the wild faces screaming in through the tinted glass made me think that as a pig going to trough I might just be dragged out, and as a meat eater myself, aborted.

On arriving at the Shriners HQ, where the pageant was to take place, we stepped on the famous red carpet. Written like that it sounds easy, but getting out of the limo with any semblance of dignity is a non-starter (those of you reading this who partied in the Seventies will have distant memories of being trapped in those bean bag seats unable to get up). Eventually after taking a deep breath each, we set off through thousands of screaming fans, who reached out to us. It seemed they all wanted to shake your hand. I obliged, aye often. One fan asked me was there any truth in the rumour that Kim Basinger's marriage was in trouble. I answered truthfully that I didn't know but for what it's worth, George and May in Renfrew are doing just fine.

In the hall at last. It was hard to take it all in. They were all there. Two rows in front sat Karl Malden. He stood up, every inch a movie star. Faye Dunaway stood up too – all night as it happened, and as I was sat behind her it became a bit of a nuisance. Back and forth she went to the toilet. Back and forth. Up and down. Back and forth. Up and down. Instead of spending all that money on her looks she should have used it on consulting a urinologist.

The Oscar statues had been lost and were only found days before the ceremony by a dustman. He was rewarded by being given a ringside seat. On being asked by Billy Crystal, the evening's compere, if he was enjoying the show, quick as a flash the man responded, 'Sure am, next year I'll be back as a director'. Gallus is gallus wherever it's practised. Then it was 'Ladies and Gentlemen, welcome to the 72nd Oscar ceremony etc. etc.'. House lights dimmed, a fanfare blared. We paid attention.

Billy Crystal exploded on to the stage and we were off. 'It's great to see so many new faces in the audience', he announced. 'And noses and eyes...'. Everyone laughed, including the New Faces. To have 'work done' is the new status symbol and plastic surgery is the growth industry in town. If that is not a kind of misnomer.

On the stage came 'Charlie's Angels', and after a bit of fluff 'that' envelope was opened.

POW!!!

'The Oscar goes to Lindy Hemming for Topsy Turvy'. The audience went wild, Lindy went into shock. My heart thumped. To see Jack

Nicholson, Michael Caine, Warren Beatty, on their feet applauding your mate is not a scene easily forgotten.

Lindy gave the shortest, and in my opinion the most genuine, speech of the night having not expected to win. Just a thought – what happens to all those long lists in the pockets of the non-winners. You know the ones, where they thank everyone from their parents through to second cousins once removed, their drama coach, personal trainer and so on up to and including the great architect himself. What if they get knocked down on leaving the theatre and some paramedic reads it to his mate. Embarrassing, eh? Never mind the dirty underwear scenario.

But to our tale, people were crowding round to congratulate – me! It must be an American thing (unless, it's a long shot, they've seen my paper-hanging). Lindy was away being interviewed by trade journals. A young lady took her seat even though I tried to explain the situation. She informed me that she and others were engaged for the evening, as seat fillers, their function to fill any empty seat whenever the occupant left to answer the call of nature. For the world's cameras no empty seat must ever be glimpsed.

On another occasion I was joined by a young man in full evening wear who, wasting no time, immediately launched into his pitch. He had this script that would be box office dynamite, all his mates liked it, and all it needed was someone, like me for instance, to put some money into the project. Boy was he sitting in the wrong seat.

I was still being congratulated as Ray Charles appeared, then Garth Brooks, Robin Williams, Isaac Hayes followed by one of those interchangeable beautiful black singers. Lindy returned with the Oscar. Everyone leaned over to touch it (tribal folk memories of a certain golden calf came to mind).

The show ended. It felt like only minutes. I went to the bar to get Lindy a drink to calm her nerves, only to discover that like the family royal, I had no money on me.

The pockets of my outfit were sewn up. This is not a dig at Scotland. That tailor in Edinburgh told me it made the suit hang better (You can't beat our friends in the capital). The man behind me promptly paid for me.

I'm so impressed – I'm thinking of having the pockets of all my suits sewn up. 'Scotty', he said. 'Your date has just joined Hollywood's chosen, and it would be my pleasure to buy her her first drink in that category'. I thanked him and in a spirit of internationalism told him if he ever found himself in Scotland I would return the favour. I then gave him Davie Cooper's address. Taking the drink I moved through the dancers in the gap advert, back to the auditorium, as I did so I held the door open for this old guy (oops! senior). He thanked me 'You're ever so gracious colonel'. I was deflated. I, by that time, had a guid conceit o' mysel and it was a bit of a come down.

Now it was the return journey along the red carpet. I was now carrying the wee golden man (aye it is heavy) and the patient fans roared themselves hoarse at the sight of him. I was asked my views on the state of the film industry, the challenge of new technologies, and much else beside. Being an old shop steward, I was giving a good account of myself until I got a bit lost bluffing about post-modernist deconstruction and the subliminal racist message contained in the dialogue of the Lion King.

Put a beggar on a horseback as they say. Eventually we arrived at the Governor's ball where we were seated beside Charles Rosen and his wife. On the table was a brown and white sculpture depicting a can of film with movie reels spewing from it. I promptly put it into my mouth. Chuck (well, we had known him for at least five minutes) looked aghast. He was the Art Director on the 'Producers' so together we sung 'Springtime for Hitler'. Have you ever tried to sing it with a mouthful of cardboard? We picked up our goody bags and left for 'the Hottest Party in Town' - Elton John's. We were met by Lindy's agent, Vanessa, who marched us straight through the partygoers to the top table. There sat the rambler Janet Street-Porter and David Furnish. He was momentarily taken aback, having last seen me drinking meths in Edinburgh. No, I made that last bit up in case you had dozed off. Elton made a great fuss of Lindy and he and she and Joan Rivers were all photographed together for some glamorous magazine. I attempted to push the young protagonist from the Sixth Sense out of my way in my excitement to get in the shot. I failed. One of Elton's entourage brought over the goody bags but I wasn't having any of it. Not tonight in my tartanry. 'How many hair straighteners do you need anyway?'. He looked amazed at the refusal and well he should have been. On the TV the following day it was announced that the goody bags at Elton's party were just that. They were valued at hundreds of dollars and contained video cameras, binoculars, expensive designed sunspecs, books, gold watched and much else besides. Ach well, I'll know next time.

A man leaned over to Lindy. 'You sure make a swell couple ma'am. Is your husband in the military?' he said. I was shrinking as he finished the sentence. I'll be visiting a certain tailor the next time I'm in Edinburgh, I can assure you of that.

Back in the hotel the now tipsy Lindy got Peter Fonda to open a bottle of Champagne he was nursing. The big easy rider raised his glass in congratulations. What an experience.

A few months later we were visiting the Queen Mary at Long Beach. Beside the great liner is a Scottish Heritage gift shop where two men in full highland dress were engaged in selling souvenirs of the magnificent ship to the throngs of tourists.

One of them yelled out in broad Glaswegian, 'Too big noo tae speak tae your auld freens'.

I looked round, taken aback at hearing the vernacular so far from home.

'Hello, Jimmy – did you see me at the Oscars?', I said.

'Oscars nothin' wee man, I worked wi' you in Govan, building the 'Jervis Bay''.

Hollywood and the Oscars seemed a million light years away.

A wee postscript. The other weekend in London, I had the Golden Man in a plastic bag (don't ask). A guy approached me and enquired where the joke shop was, where the Oscars are sold.

I was going to tell him the truth but it would have involved too much name dropping, and I'm not into that.

A Wee Heat An' That

The painter looked along at the hundreds of windows still to be painted. He sighed a mixture of despair and resignation. Perched, as he was, on top of the thirty-foot three splice ladder, he had to concentrate on balancing himself and making sure he could perform the job in hand. He tapped on the window. It was opened by a middle-aged woman who almost dragged him inside, so glad was she to have company. Living in one of the new housing estates had lots of advantages, but she 'missed the old familiarity of her previous tenement' she said.

'I'll put the kettle on and you'll have a wee biscuit?'

'You don't have to, missus. We go down to our howff at the end of the road and we get a wee heat an' that.'

'Oh, ah can gie you a wee heat an' that.'

The painter was too numb to acknowledge the come-on. His feet ached. The spiel among the painters was that you could always tell a ladder man – his feet were curled round like a budgie's. Well, his feet ached and he was numb with cold.

He dipped the brush and noticed how thick the material was, owing to the cold. Then, applying it, he was on automatic pilot, where he had perfected the brush stroke and could have painted in his sleep, which, in a way, he did. Often, on completion of a window, he genuinely couldn't remember a thing about it.

The whistle blew for the break and he descended the ladder at speed. This action could be seen repeated the length of the street as other painters responded to the whistle. They all made their way to the howff and the patter merchants among them used the time to hone their story-telling skills. Some of the older hands kept to themselves, having heard most of the tales a thousand times over, and preferred to walk in silence and enjoy a smoke. The break over the painters wandered back to work and, having thawed out some, our man had had time to think of the woman's welcome offer.

On returning to his ladder he blew his dripping nose to make the most of his looks and began his ascent, which he did quite fast having had his bones heated.

He rapped on the window. No response.

He knocked a bit louder. This time he could hear footsteps approaching.

Clearing his throat, he announced 'I'm back. And, yes, I'll take up your kind offer of a wee heat…an' that'

He laughed out loud thinking this will make a good story for tomorrow's break.

The window opened almost throwing the painter off the ladder.

'I'll give you a WEE HEAT…an' THAT' shouted a very angry man.

The painter had injured his hand as the window swung open. He had dropped his brush and the paint pot was already buried in the garden. The painter, in pain, made a fast descent, baffled by his change in fortune.

On reaching the bottom, he was surrounded, to his surprise, by a crowd of his workmates, all laughing.

'What the…?' he began.

'During the break we rushed back and moved your ladder a couple of windows down. As they all look the same, we knew you wouldn't notice, until too late. But what a result!

'Bastards' he replied, laughing.

A Friend In Need Is...

He held his breath and slowly tip-toed past the pensioner's door. He could hear her moving about. He didn't hesitate, but moved purposely on. He had been caught many times before; sent on missions, usually for medicines, and he had come to the conclusion that much and all as he wanted to help, he couldn't just be available just when she desired.

She moaned theatrically and whined when asking for his assistance. How sincere she was he could never guess. What if he declined her requests and she succumbed; could he live with that?

He allowed himself a smile; made it, he thought. Then the door opened. Oh, no.

'Is that you?' she said.

'Eh, aye it is'.

'I wonder if you could do me a wee favour'.

'Well, I was going to…' he tailed off. Another defeat.

She invited him in to her well-kept apartment.

'I'm out of aspirin and I just can't get to sleep without them. If you could get me some I would be so grateful'

She handed him the money and escorted him to the door, grimacing as she did so.

It was lightly drizzling. He mumbled a cheerio and headed out on his task. He waited for a bus. None came. He was frozen now and, checking he had enough cash with him, decided to get the next taxi that appeared. He waited what seemed like hours and no wonder – it *was* hours. Giving up, he started to walk through the rain. Eventually, a mini-cab stopped to drop off a fare; he ran before the car moved off. The driver was listening to the football on the radio; he waved our man to enter and, when given the address, set off.

They arrived at the chemist that the pensioner had requested. It was closed. He kept the cab and read the notice in the chemist's window stating that in an emergency go to the following address. They did. And it too was closed. His heart sank. Same story as the first place, but without the notice in the window.

'I'm off home, friend' said the cabbie. 'I should have been off hours ago, but you looked in such a state that I couldn't refuse you'. The cabbie drove off.

Now the evening was turning in to a drama. He walked in the still pouring rain, but, experiencing the cold, realised that he was on a fruitless exercise. Still competing with himself, he vowed that he would not return empty-handed.

He met a group of young people, all laughing and enjoying life. She must have been young once, he thought. But he had only ever known her as a chronic, sick pensioner. Maybe that's the fate that awaits us all. The young team told him of an all-night chemist that definitely would be open, but it's a bit of a way away. He thanked them and checked his cash; there was insufficient for another cab journey.

Had the first chemist been open he would have bought the aspirin and been back home in time to enjoy the rest of the evening; as it was, the night was a dud. Everyone would either be watching the match at home, or in company in some warm pub up the town. Enough, he thought. The night's over. Let me complete this mission and I'll never get caught by her ever again. With those thoughts keeping his spirits up he set off at a brisk pace for the chemists.

He found it, eventually. It was, indeed, open twenty-four hours and, as a consequence, the place was full of addicts waiting in line and talking absolute gibberish to one another. He got the aspirin and, feeling quite pleased with himself, set about the return journey. The streets were deserted now and a chill wind had got up. Best to keep moving, he thought. At least she will be grateful and this made him feel good inside. Not exactly altruistic, but a wee glow of pride.

In front of him, a lively crowd were piling into a van. He asked was there room for one more and, when they agreed, he leapt in, thankful to be out of the cold.

'Where to, chief?' one of the crowd asked in mock cabbie speak.

‘Anywhere, where I can get a bus’

Luckily they were driving in his general direction and he thanked them, really thanked them when they dropped him off only a few miles from home.

Still raining and wet through, he now realised how tired he was too. It had been hours since he had set off. He willed his tired legs into a semi-jog. He would run home, deliver the goods and be home in jig time. The thought buoyed him up and he soon reached his block. Her light was still on so he knocked the door. After releasing the numerous bolts, she opened the door to him in her nightdress.

He triumphantly handed over the package and waited for the praise that would surely be his reward.

She took it from him and sighed.

‘But I only take the soluble, son!’

The Man Previously Called The Blade

As the painters filed out of the hut after the break, I hung back and confronted the BLADE about his arrears.

I was the shop steward and it was my duty to inspect the union cards and, if any member wasn't up to date with his dues, to remind them that they would be out of benefit.

The BLADE – the nickname was axiomatic and it was with a feeling of apprehension that I approached all 6'3' of him.

He told me to 'fuck off!' No explanation, no excuses. He picked up his bag, slung it over his shoulder and briskly marched off.

The other members of the squad watched the event. Whatever the outcome – they didn't care one way or another whether the big man was out of benefit or not – this incident would, at least, break the monotony of a long, dull day. For my part, I couldn't lose face. Being a shop steward is putting yourself up for a baiting. The labour force knows that you are their representative, but any authority must be challenged and they perceive a steward as having authority, however limited.

The next day I held a brief meeting, highlighting the fact that the management were flexing their muscles for a test of power and it would be wise to be fully paid-up members of the union as a form of protection. I looked at the BLADE as I spelled out the message.

Meeting over and we're going to our respective boats. The BLADE passes me and out of the side of his mouth he mutters 'You're claimed'.

The next day I have a quiet word with him and explain, in mock seriousness the position; his, mine, the union's and the management's. Again a few painters are hanging around and just want an EVENT. He responds to the crowd and again refuses to bring his card up to date. He is pleased to be the centre of attention (however briefly) with his fellow workers and is smiling, well-pleased with his stand.

I turned serious now – life is tough, especially in the yards – 'Tomorrow big man or you're out the door'.

Next day, I'm in the circular gun turret painting electrical cables – their functions I never could guess at. The BLADE approaches and neatly places the considerable sum of his arrears beside me – in pennies.

I refuse even to count them.

'They're legal tender' he states, obviously quoting a line from one of the painters, not having the brains to put that sentence together for himself. Oh, those below deck lawyers, I think to myself.

'You can just go and change your 'legal tender' into paper money and we'll all be happy.'

He opens his bag and produces a kitchen knife of terrifying proportions.

'This is for you, pal' he snarls as he puts the coins back in the bag.

At night, as the painters change out of their overalls some enquire, innocent-like, if the arrears have been paid. I ignore the group of malcontents, who have latched on to this incident. An event was an event.

'I'll see you at the gate' the BLADE snarled as he marched out of the hut.

Heart pounding, but up for it, I followed. Not rushing, but trying to think out a strategy; trying to get out of it wasn't an option. On reaching the gate there was no BLADE there. Adrenalin up, I was at a loss to comprehend the situation. I gave up and went home.

Next day I went to another gate, thinking that the BLADE had gone to this one by mistake – no BLADE.

This exercise was repeated a few more times, with the malcontents baying the message that the issue should be settled once and for all. The excitement was infecting the rest of the men, who were now showing an interest in the outcome. I realised that deep down the BLADE wasn't for it. He kept picking a different gate at night, but always the one I wasn't at. The EVENT wasn't going to happen after all and the attention span of the painters slipped slowly away. The monotony continued.

The BLADE marched out of the hut the following evening thinking that, although there had been no outcome, he had won and he would bring in his money, not wanting to be a target for the management. Wee

Goudie, all five foot three of him, followed.

'Hey, you!'

The BLADE turned and was immediately attacked. Goudie had produced a hammer from somewhere and, in one movement, had leapt and smashed the big man's nose to pulp. The BLADE's knees buckled and he fell down slowly, like a demolished building. When his face reached the same level as Goudie's he was head-butted. End of story.

It's that old 'you never know where it will come from.'

The painters had got their EVENT.

Venceremos

The Chilean coup was complete. Pinochet was the boss. Those who were fortunate enough fled the country. Some had ended up in Glasgow and, being considered fairly exotic in that proletarian city, were in big demand at parties.

The labour movement, to its credit, had played a leading role in forcing the authorities to find accommodation for these new émigrés. Many in the Communist Party took them into their homes as full family members. In time, the new arrivals could party with the best in that fun-loving city.

Anyhow, this particular evening the academic left had organised a soiree for the Chileans. A night of Chilean music, food and culture to better the understanding between the two peoples; and with the additional function of raising money to assist in the removal of the dictator and a return home of the exiles.

The very drunk political activist was heading in the direction of the festivities. He had finished his week's toil in the shipyards, got cleaned up and suited, and was out to enjoy himself: be a king for the few hours of freedom that was his due.

He hadn't been invited; the reason given by the predominantly middle-class academics, organisers of the event, was that it had been impossible to get in touch with him with the necessary details, such as location, time, etc. of the beano.

The real reason was, in truth, the comrade was mad on the drink and so outrageous when in such a condition that the more refined of the party-goers simply didn't want to spend their time in his company.

But our brave activist had, by a variety of stratagems and animal cunning, discovered the whereabouts of the evening's bash and was heading there.

The way the middle-class supporters of socialism lived their lives was indicative of the way society worked. Yes, we would one day be all equal, but not too soon, please. Give us a chance and anyhow it was only a theory – wasn't it?

The activist – we'll call him Gordon (the term 'activist' sounds so robotic) - was weaving his way towards the close mouth now. In his left hand, a plastic carrier bag containing the three bottles of cheap wine that would facilitate his admission into the party.

He knew he desperately needed a good opener. That was a must. It was essential that his entrance be good. These academics kept the women to themselves. No sharing in that department, comrade. He stood for another rest. Taking a bottle out of his cargo, he topped up his intake. Now I'm getting somewhere, he thought. Yes, I'm on the right track. No swearing, that's as read, but difficult to carry out, it's habit. He looked at his reflection in the stair landing window. Not too bad, young Gordon, he smiled. No vomit or spittle in evidence on the jacket, can't be too careful. What the ladies judged acceptable on the front of a lecturer's shirt was a definite no-no when sported by one of the lower orders. Some things were not addressed in the books of political philosophy, but were, nevertheless, important guidelines, just the same.

'Got it!' Gordon said out loud. 'I'll make my intro in Spanish…what was that word? *...venc… ven…* It's gone, too bad. There's always '*Che'*, but everyone knows that. Where's the novelty there?'

He gave the problem his fullest, but drunk, attention. '*Viva, Allend…* come on, Gordon, you've been to these places'. He had been an engineer for a time in the merchant navy and had, indeed, visited most of South America. One step up and then he tried to walk up the last two before having to stop and compose his thoughts, yet again.

'*Monte... monte…*something… Yes, he was getting somewhere. Sure. On the boat. We said it all the time…yes, *monte... v... d...monteV.D.* Fuck, can't say that. Uruguay…you're a guy. That's out, too. Come on, man! Spanish… you know millions of words. I shouldn't drink… nearly there… *Donde est la…* '

He must make his entrance a knock-out. The party has been going for some time now and everyone will have made friends, paired off even. Come on, time is of the utmost importance, he thought.

'*La lotta contin…*' Hell, he used that one every day in the yard.

He looked up at the next landing. The door. Gordon straightened up. Drew a deep breath.

Gordon's antenna was working overtime trying to decipher where, in his drunken state, he could hear the music and laughter coming from. He attempted to climb the stairs; harder than he thought. During working hours he was a tireless, veritable work beast. Also, whenever election time arrived he was observed to be the fastest at delivering election addresses up and down stairs with ferocious speed. But when he switched off during his drinking sessions he lost all physical grace. This was such a time.

He put one foot in front of the other with intense deliberation and climbed up a few steps, only to stumble back down again. He thought of Lenin's work: *Two Steps Forward; Three Steps Back*. He smiled to himself, but couldn't alter his present condition.

Inside the party things were in full swing. The academic lecturers engaged with the Chileans in Spanish, ostensibly to make the exiles feel more at home, but, in reality, to impress their fellow party members, party goers and especially the young female students who were always to be found at such dos. All the young ladies would have defined themselves as liberated feminists, but, in truth, were laying out their stalls in the hope of catching some lecturer (never mind that the latter may be married and have an ex-liberated woman of his own stuck at home minding the kids that evening).

The wine was being consumed with gusto and the air was filled by many '*ole*'s and cries of '*venceremos*', '*patria e muerto*' and such like, but not from Chilean throats. Some party-goers even gilded the lily a bit by attempting to add a lisp to their Spanish, just for added piquancy. The young ladies lapped this up. What joy!

Gordon was approaching the main event. He could feel it. Only another flight of stairs and he was there. Nirvana at last. More wine and, yes, the studentessi. But first get into good shape. His drunk brain attempted to make sense of it all. Then he knocked the door with authority.

The door was opened by a slender young lady. She opened it wide enough for Gordon to see by her into the wild, happy scene. He couldn't contain his exuberance any longer.

Stepping inside, he raised his clenched fist, threw back his head and roared out:

'CARMEN MIRANDA!'

In a flash he knew he had fucked up. One day he must attend one of these things sober. But not tonight. Tonight he needed more drink, and fast.

'Ach, what the hell' he thought, 'Next time…'

The Karate Kid

I was working on a film set. I could hardly believe it. Me, an ex-building trade operative, ex-yard man. I was now being spoken to in a civilised way by young ladies with hyphenated names. After a lifetime of being barked and snarled at by ugly foremen, it was a joy to be requested to do my allotted tasks from a young lady with perfect teeth. And when completed, to be thanked. Oh, those middle-class girls.

The movie industry is not too dissimilar to a battleground, minus the live ammo. On a set there are hours of inactivity, followed by intense, heart-pounding periods of sheer mad vigorous labour. There is the adrenalin kicking in, then having to attempt some normality, only for it all to be repeated, yet again.

The analogy of a battle is also demonstrated in the fact that scores of people with a multiplicity of skills have assembled for one purpose only. The director, akin to a general, is omnipotent and can change his ideas on a whim; and does so.

This was a day when he exercised his authority and decided that the wall I had just painted was wrong. No ifs or buts, it had to be repainted to aid his overview on how the film should look.

I jumped to action. No time to clean the brushes; new ones are needed. I hurriedly looked round at various onlookers: those who had completed their tasks and those waiting to do so. I spotted a 'Barbour Jacket' from the art department. Ex-Art School, with the trick first name: Jo, Su, Bea, Val, Di, Ta, Zara or similar. Certainly not Bunty, Teresa or Senga.

'Quick! Run next door to the newsagent's and buy a couple of brushes' I said, but in the heat of the battle forgetting the mandatory 'please'.

The onlookers drifted away to a more exciting place to loiter. Who wants to watch paint wet or, indeed, dry when there are soundmen and camera crews, not to mention the actors, in the vicinity.

I had sheeted the floor and was up a pair of steps when a Barbour-clad hand thrust the brushes in my direction. No problem. After years of painting I knew when a turn of speed was called for. I went to war instantly.

In minutes I had finished my task. The First Assistant gave the shout and the whole unit moved to where I had stood seconds ago.

The tension was now with the actors, the Director, the Director of Photography and the sound squad; so, I could make myself scarce and return to my previous state of waiting until called for again.

The Barbour-wearer approached.

'A word' she demanded, glaring at me.

Baffled, I made a gesture of incomprehension.

'You insulted me in front of my peers and I simply won't have it, especially from a painter.'

'Painter' – she spat this out like an expletive.

'I can't think, I…' I was mumbling.

'Oh, yes. You knew exactly what you were doing. Sending me to the shop like a little girl.'

'Oh, that's what's bothering you, is it? Get on wi' your knitting an' gie me peace.'

She went berserk, actually foaming at the mouth, eyes bulging, face contorted.

'Over here, you.' She literally spat out the words indicating a piece of spare ground.

I obeyed, wondering what kind of dressing down was on offer. Those film people.

She, at once, adopted a karate stance, waving her hands this way and that. I stood watching, entranced. I laughed.

'You won't be laughing in a minute' she said as she chopped the air. 'I'm highly-trained. I'm part of the women's self-defence group and I know how to deal with bullying men like you.'

'I'll break your fucking jaw' I said jokingly.

‘We’ll see about that’ she replied.

I turned from the combat (didn’t I say it was like a battlefield) and went back to continue my waiting. This is a strange industry I thought as I mentally compared it with the shipyards.

She was still standing flailing her arms around karate-style.

‘COWARD!’ she screeched.

The Frozen Moment

It was a raw, keen, winter's morning in the shipyard and sounds carried further than usual, with the sharpness and clarity that is a characteristic of such days. As it was a Monday morning, the painter worked in that trance-like silence that is common to that first part of the first day of any week.

Like the other men working alongside him, the painter was deep in his thoughts, to block out the harshness of his surroundings. He relived the events of the weekend and replayed them over and over again, like a continuous video tape, editing out the less-exciting parts until he had distilled for himself a repertoire of experiences that gave him a glow; from which he drew a strength of sorts.

Every so often he was jolted back to reality by the sudden whine of a drill or by the clang of metal plates crashing against each other nearby. They were made noticeable only on account of their nearness to him, as all over the yard in fits and spurts, a multiplicity of sounds assailed the eardrums. The cacophony was made bearable because it represented work and therefore a regular wage-packet.

Building a ship required all types of steel plate. It was the painter's task to coat them with yellow chromate to prevent corrosion. Well, if not in truth to prevent it, at least to slow up the rusting process until the ship was launched and delivered.

The metal was extremely cold to the touch and he continually changed hands, as after only a few minutes holding the brush it became unbearable. At any given point, he kept a hand in his overall pocket and counted the time until he would have to change hands. He was frozen numb to this routine. Hunched against the draughts in the passage-way at the tail-end of the ship he sank deeper into despair as the morning wore on. In these conditions an eight-hour working day seemed an eternity.

In such a situation, even the weekend fought a losing battle to keep at the centre of his thoughts. As time passed, the weekend could no longer stay in contention and gave up, leaving the painter with the blankness that only a wage-slave fully appreciates.

'A whole week of this' he said aloud 'to support a table and four chairs'.

He was so filled with despair that he just had to stop painting for a second to recuperate. He straightened up, put the brush across the top of the paint-pot and shuffled to the ship's side. Leaning against the rail, he looked around him. It was an unusually quiet period in the shipyard, as occasionally happened when hole-borers went to the shore-side to change their drills and the caulkers to draw out new chisels. The caulkers used this opportunity to fix their air-hoses to the main air supply (called 'the pig' because of the row of teats along its length, resembling a sow lying on her side). This contraption only emitted the slightest hiss, which emphasised the quietness of the frozen yard.

Suddenly, a lone voice rang out. Clear as a hammer striking unyielding metal and, as it was winter, the voice carried to the entire yard.

'Hi, Ho o o o o o o o o o o o o o o o o o...'

The voice held the note long; pure as crystal. There was silence and then the voice again.

'Hi, Ho o o o o o o o o o o o o o o o o o...'

All the workers who heard it were instantly caught in its spell. They were transported back in time to the golden days of the Saturday matinee.

There are sounds which can trigger off memories and this unknown singer produced such a sound. It is a gift which can unlock the floodgates; and he did. He struck gold with that opening burst of song. It contained it all: the cheap, sticky sweets; the stench of piss that nipped the eyes; the cinnamon fag burning, rather than being actually smoked; and the absolutely indescribable feeling of 'being in the gang'. Belonging. So potent is that experience that, contrary to the Bible, when we are men we don't put away all our childish things; indeed, some feelings we guard and nurture forever. This emotion is of that kind.

The painter smiled and a good feeling flooded through him. Looking around, he observed that his workmates were also smiling. They smiled at each other without embarrassment; each understanding the other's thoughts. The voice had galvanised them all. They were all back with the seven dwarfs in Snow White.

The voice rang out again, but this time the singer wasn't alone. The entire labour force was singing now:

'Hi, ho, hi, ho,

It's off to work we go.

We work all day, we get no pay,

Hi, ho, hi, ho, hi ho, hi ho.'

Then the explosion of laughter roared out, that welded each man to his neighbour.

'Aye, this is what it's all about' thought the painter as he picked up his brush and resumed painting. The day didn't seem so cold now, nor as long.

The unknown soloist had created a magic every bit as intense as Disney's and had, for a brief period, made the brutal act of building a ship in winter tolerable.

The Kitty

Monologue - contains not only bad language, but bad grammar.

Fuck them an' the kitty. Ah wid hiv pit in but Ah'm aye carryin' them. Ah'm masel'. They can a' go an' fuck themsel. Is that the rain – might hiv known. It's wan o' they days. That's a' Ah need – rain. Fuckin' Karma, eh. Some other bastard will be getting' the sun an' here's me walkin' in the rain a' by masel. Swings an' roundabouts ye hear them say. Swings fuck a'. Ah aye get the wrang end. Them an' their kitty – I wis just kiddin' Ah wis skint but then the silly wee pound fell oot ma jacket. That wis a' Ah needed. Ah telt them it wis a joke a wee bit o' a gee up but they widnae buy it – no' them naebody listens to me anyway. But Ah knew ma tea wis oot. So Ah guyed it there an' then. Ah wis bombed oot an' Ah knew it. Ah'm no' carin'. Ah got by afore Ah teamed up wi' them an' Ah'll get by withoot them the noo. O.K. So Ah wis oot o' order no weighin' in but we've a' done it. Them an' a'. An' another thing whit aboot a' the times Ah stuck in ma tank when they had heehaw. But oh no naebody remembers that. Ah put in plenty over the years – a' forgotten. Wan smelly stroke an' Ah'm bombed oot. See if Ah could turn the clock back Ah would hiv weighed right in no problem. But ye cannae turn that old clock back it would be the jinkies if ye could but Ah would turn it back way afore them. Ah would turn it back tae when Ah hud a hoose aye an' her tae. But ye cannae. Full stop. Period. Kaput. That fuckin' rain. Whit a result – never comes by itsel' luck. Naw aye in bunnels o' three an' getting cauld tae. An aye the billet is oot that means a skipper. Skipperin's OK when yer a boay but this is right oot o' order. Ah should hiv turned my collar up but too late noo. If Ah dae it noo it'll be wet. An' when Ah dae find some doorway ah'll need to watch that it disnae touch ma neck. But that's no' the worst part o' it if Ah'm honest it's bein' on ma ain, ma Jack Jones naebody tae hae the crack wi' nae patter. Mibbe if Ah can find some dough Ah could get a couple o' bottles an' just wander back intae the team. Ah widnae talk first. Oh no Ah wid just act casual but Ah wid put wan o' the bottles doon an' Ah bet ye in a couple o' minutes wan o' them wid come across och Ah don't care. Maybe some punter'll gie me a few bob. Ah should hive turnt the clock back. Ach Ah wid be playin' Junior noo well maybe no Junior but Ah could still be in good shape. An' who knows mibbe I could hiv been workin' in Canada, the States even. These bastards will be well on by noo – jammy bastard but Ah'll no' forget this no way. The minute Ah get a turn Ah'm aff – Ah'll no' tell no cunt Ah'll be Joe the Toff. Mibbe Ah'll jist phone wan o' thae days frae somewhere – This rain right noo Ah'd settle for a dry night. Ah could find that school an' see if the janny wid let me in tae the boiler room get the heid doon. A' he'd want is a coupla fags. Fuck Ah've nane. Swings and roundabouts Ah'm fucked again. See if Ah win the Lottery Ah'm history man nae kiddin' bit noo Ah'll settle fur a doorway that naebody's pished in.

To Err Is But... Keeping Warm

'Ambulance Room, well?'

'We cannae. We were there yesterday.'

'So what?'

'Our names will be in the book.'

'Safety store?'

'Again? We're no' long back...naw.'

'George's hut?'

'We're barred!'

'How?'

'The Ouija board... no remember?'

'Oh, aye, so we are.'

We worked on in silence for a time, but the cold wind was doing its worst and our eyes were watering and the cold coming up from the steel decks was unrelenting even though we were stamping our feet continually. The fact that the boots were steel-toe-capped didn't help. The bleakness of a winter's day in a shipyard has to be experienced to appreciate what the absence of colour does to the senses.

We were painting with grey paint on top of many coats of grey paint. We would have bluffed it out in the past and just pretended we had re-painted the bulkheads, if it had not been for the fact that the inspectors carried a gadget that when placed on the surface could calculate accurately how many coats of paint had been applied. All around us was grey. The sky. The sheds. The cranes. Even the very atmosphere. Sensory deprivation. And is that not a recognised torture? And the cold – always the cold.

Eventually, I spoke through the rags round my face - this feeble attempt at keeping my face warm. Normally I wouldn't have wrapped the rags anywhere near my face and the fact that printed on the corner of one of them was the name of the nearest hospital, the Southern General, didn't help. But needs must and I was akin to a Bedouin in the desert, except for the cold.

Again the silence. We worked on occasionally looking at one another and shaking our heads. Willie was wrapped up identical to myself, but he had stuffed the Daily Record under his hard hat. A good move that, I thought. The Record was a fairly substantial newspaper, being full of the usual shite - crosswords, cartoons, comic strips, cookery recipes, photographs of half-naked nonentities, quizzes, letters to the editor on such subjects as cruelty to donkeys and how, after a lifetime's work, they should be kept in luxury. All this irony was passing through my addled brain; my critical faculties having shut down ages past, what with the cold and the paint fumes. I had to conclude though that Willie's paper was a better investment in such conditions than my flimsy, two-page Morning Star.

'Oh, fuck this!' I eventually said. 'I'm off somewhere…anywhere.'

'I'll join you in case you get lost' volunteered Willie.

With that we placed our paint pots and brushes in a recess in the ship's side and walked off the ship. The very act of moving put some life back into us and we even laughed at our predicament.

I took stock of our position. The boat would have to manage without us for a spell, but where to go? We talked about going to the paint store, but we would have been in real trouble, as our Foreman would have had to leave his warm office to see what we wanted and that would have been a Federal offence. We walked aimlessly, our brains not yet thawed. Eventually, we came to a building at the far end of the yard. Normally we wouldn't have been in this area; it not being on any of our usual skiving routes.

'There will definitely be heat in there' said Willie. 'Offices are aye well looked after.'

Willie was a Govan man, with all that that means. It's hard to describe, but I'm a wee Maryhill man and I can tell you there is a difference. Well, I can't articulate it, but I know there is a certain something… a certain… ach, forget it… Ah just know. We were mated up with each other a few years back when we both found ourselves on a punishment job. Willie was a tough guy and could look after himself. And I? Well, I was a wee guy who could look after Willie looking after himself. We were a good team: better, stronger than our individual parts.

Semmit and Drawers they had named us. This is always a good sign in a shipyard. It means, in effect, you haven't lost your individuality in the five thousand man broth.

We looked through the window at the corridors inside; no-one inside. The heat from within could be felt on the glass.

'I'm in' said Willie.

I followed, there was no argument. We entered the building and the heat made us laugh.

'This'll do for me.'

'Me and all.'

We proceeded cautiously along the place and climbed the stairs in front of us. At the top was a door. The notice on it read: TOP SECRET. ABSOLUTELY NO ADMISSION. Then in smaller print the information that jail terms of varying lengths were to be had, etc. etc. etc..

We entered.

There was a hum from some gadget taking photographs of a sheet of drawings. This was of no interest to us. We were looking for somewhere to hide until we were warm again. We spotted a few white coats hanging on coat hooks and, taking off our face rags, put them on.

We stopped beside a hot chocolate machine and put in a few coins for a cup of the stuff. The clatter the machine made as it brewed up the mixture had us on alert. It was all very James Bond. We could hear voices, but didn't know what direction they were coming from. The voices suddenly appeared beside us. We nodded a greeting and walked on, making a face at each other.

This was the life. For a brief moment we were enjoying the luxuries that other people took for the norm. We sipped the hot drink and pretended we had every right to be in the building. We were now back to our true selves. The hot drink and being out of the harsh weather had worked wonders.

The madness had returned. Madness? You might ask.

Well, the quickest, simplest explanation is that painters, by the very act of applying toxic paint, have altered the composition of their brains. Then there is the desire to find a laugh, no matter the circumstances, and the human need to break the continuity of monotony for however short a period – to save your sanity. Then there is the perverse tickle of excitement to be had when you're up to mischief.

'Ah, fuck it. I'm for a laugh here' Willie said. He picked up a drawing and acted out what he believed a scientist would behave like. He scratched his head over some unsolvable problem, and then chewed the end of a pencil that he had found in the lab coat. We were now giggling like two wee boys who had found themselves in the janitor's storeroom all those years ago back at school.

He appeared from nowhere. Well, that's not literally true; he appeared from somewhere that we had not thought of. He was some kind of security man and a quick look would have told any observer that he was not too smart and a jobsworth of the First Division.

'Right, you two. What's your game?'

'Us?' I said, fully under the madness spell. 'We're taking this drawing to the Chinese restaurant along the road. He said he'd see us all right.'

'You're what?' he screeched.

'You know, red China an' that' said Willie, up for a laugh.

I rolled up a drawing and theatrically put it under my arm. 'This should be worth a couple of Chow Meins, at least' I said.

In a flash the security man had rugby-tackled me. He's locked fast round my legs below the knee and is now shouting. I can't make out the actual words coming out of his red, distorted face, but I know we must get out…and fast.

Willie is dragging the man off and we're laughing at the incongruity of the scene. Between us we prise him off and make for the exit, our hot drink having spilled during the encounter. We're now running and he is blowing a whistle – a whistle, for Christs sakes. We're laughing, but running like our lives depend on it. We open the door – freedom! Now we're back in the familiar territory of the yard. It's still freezing, but as we throw off the white coats we realise that we are warm and we've had a wee adventure.

We're soon back on the boat. We pick up our kit and paint. In the distance we hear a faint whistle, then it stops and the yard is back to its grey, normal appearance. We work in silence, then Willie, with a burst of laughter says:

'Red China, eh?'

I laugh with him. A wee adventure between a Govan man and a wee Maryhill man.

Once Upon A Time

Once upon a time. How often have you seen those words in recent times? Not too often, eh? So do tales and fables no longer happen in our busy, materialist world? I'm going to tell you a modern fairy tale with a twist – this one is TRUE.

Once upon a time, in a land far away, there lived a family comprising of Mum, Dad and their beautiful five-year-old daughter. Dad was an energetic construction engineer who owned his company outright. He and his wife had frugally saved, never approaching the banks for help, so consequently it had taken them longer than they had planned for, but one day they owned the entire firm, with all the bulldozers, earth-moving JCB's, etc.. Although the company was now of a modest size, they had purchased a crane painted a very fairy-tale powder blue that their daughter had chosen. Life was good and the house had more than its fair share of laughter.

One day, after breakfast, Dad set off for the building site, as he had conscientiously done since long before he was the boss. When he had been employed by others it was a daily habit that he never, ever thought of stopping. As he waved goodbye he could still hear his wife and daughter laughing in the kitchen and he was well-pleased with the world.

His reverie was brought to a halt as he nearly tripped over a middle-aged woman asleep outside his front door. Startled, she woke and mumbled something he couldn't catch. Then she got up and ran off. Strange, he thought, but forgot the incident during the day's work.

A few days later the experience was repeated, but this time he indicated for the woman to join him in the house. At first, she hesitated, a bit fearful. Then she went in with him to the kitchen. His wife and child were surprised, but not alarmed, and asked what the woman would like for breakfast. On being told, she was made comfortable sitting beside the daughter, who took to the stranger immediately.

‘What’s your name?’ enquired Dad. The woman shook her head.

‘Where do you live?’ he continued and many other questions. But the woman only shook her head in response.

‘I’m off to work’ he finally announced, ‘but finish your breakfast. Don’t rush.’ Then he was away.

On his return in the evening, as he entered, he heard the usual laughter, only this time there were three voices. A home shouldn’t have this much joy he smiled to himself as he entered the kitchen, which was the hub of the house where life was lived. There sat the woman playing a childish game with the daughter as the wife cooked the evening meal. He noted that the table was set for four.

He got cleaned up and prepared to continue with his questions with the stranger, but a slight sign from his wife indicated that he should stop. He did so at once and handed the woman the teapot, enquiring if she took milk or sugar.

She shook her head, ‘I don’t know.’

He ignored her and poured milk into her cup and passed her the sugar bowl. The child moved ever closer to her new friend and placed her favourite book between them. She pointed out her favourite colour – powder blue – and made up a child’s story around it. The woman put her arm around the daughter and joined in, embellishing the tale further. Firm friends.

‘I’ve invited her to stay, to live here for a while, until she finds herself’ declared the wife.

The Dad frowned, but said nothing.

The wife went on: ‘She can be in the end bedroom for now.’

He knew not to argue. One look at the three of them convinced him that everything would be fine. As the laughter continued, he understood that it was going to be all right. The woman had moist eyes and one tear escaped, but she said nothing.

Years later, with the daughter now a young lady attending university and the now white-haired woman still with them, he is off to work as usual. The laughter still comes from the kitchen, where his wife is good-naturedly addressing the daughter's modern outfit. The woman, as always, joins in on the daughter's side. What could possibly go wrong, he thought; I'm blessed.

This day would be different.

On assembling the powder blue crane a bolt sheared off and a section of the crane slipped, removing a man's arm. The Dad took quick action – at once he phoned for an ambulance, then climbed up to the man and comforted him as best he could, stopped all further work and sadly made his way home.

When he entered the house the normal laughter ceased as everyone, on seeing his face, understood that something terrible had happened. That evening, the meal was eaten in silence. Dad only pushed his dinner around on the plate, all the time repeating 'poor man' 'poor man'. He eventually excused himself and went to the small cabinet where all official documents were kept. He found what he was searching for – the insurance policy. Relieved to have found it he said:

'This will ensure that the poor man won't suffer financially. His arm? Well, that's gone. That's a tragedy, but at least the insurance settlement will give him some form of security over and above the job I'll find him in the firm. It was nobody's fault the accident happened, bu that's why we pay insurance.'

He let out an audible gasp. The policy had lapsed, but only by a few days.

'I'm normally so precise, but lately I've been a bit rushed and it slipped my mind. They'll understand that in all the years I've been with them I've never defaulted' he thought. He phoned the insurance company. A young lady's voice, eager and officious, noted down his particulars…and then announced that he was out of luck as his policy had expired. He stuttered about never having claimed a single thing in all the years he had been insured by them. It was futile. The law was the law and if he wished to challenge the company and dispute the interpretation of the policy that was his right. No question. And with that she cheerfully wished him a lovely day. He slumped down, phone in hand, dumb with shock.

A few days later, the bombshell he dreaded. The employee's lawyer's letter arrived informing him that, since he was under-insured, he was asking the court to seize all his equipment, including the powder-blue crane, the entire company assets.

He dropped the letter. 'I'm finished. What has it all been for? I know it's worse for the poor man, but… but…'

He couldn't continue. He left the room so that the family couldn't see his tears. There was no laughter to be heard in the house any more. Then the equipment was all towed away, to be auctioned off. It was all so final.

The weeks went by in a daze. They were sitting at breakfast one morning. The daughter was helping to clear some of the things away before she was off to university. The wife was absent-mindedly putting things here and there, just to keep herself occupied. Dad sat as usual, now in a kind of coma. Unshaven, a bit unkempt, but he didn't know what to be about. As someone who had never missed a day of work, never been late, it all seemed so hopeless now, so why try. It was so out of character that the others glided by him not wishing to cause him any discomfort. Then the old woman spoke:

'I can help.'

No one responded. She repeated herself, only louder:

'I THINK I CAN HELP.'

This time she was noticed, but not taken seriously. She began to speak, slowly at first, then she talked non-stop:

'I'm very, very rich' she began. 'I'm from one of the wealthiest families in the country and I'm worth untold millions in my own right. I detested the entire greedy, unthankful whole lot of them and never fitted in with their rapacious ways. I was always slightly fragile and I had some kind of breakdown when you took me in.'

'Why didn't you tell us at the time?' asked Dad, puzzled.

'I didn't know who or where I was' she replied.

'When did you realise all this?' Dad enquired.

'Oh, years ago' she smiled. 'But I thought if I divulge it it would change our relationship and I didn't want that to happen. This is, and has been, the happiest I have ever been and I wouldn't do anything to alter it.'

I knew it! I knew it all along!' said the daughter. 'I just felt it somehow. Such things happen.'

'Yes, in your dreams.' Dad was earnest now: 'What are we going to do?'

'I've told you. The money is yours. To do with as you wish.'

Later, when they all knew the truth and the woman had taken them all to a smart bank in the city, she made her assets over to him.

'What's to stop us throwing you out now?' he joked.

'You took me in to your lovely home when I was only a woman sleeping on your doorstep. You never knew me, never enquired of my business. You saw me one human being to another and never judged, but shared your wonderful hospitality with me – it touched me then as it touches me today. They all hugged – a real family. The bank manager stood aside, embarrassed.

The daughter wrote this story for her thesis and was marked down. Her lecturer declared it a fairy tale and not a worthy piece of literature. She wrote an entirely fictional story and was given the highest mark in the establishment. When she related this round the kitchen table the house, once again, was filled with laughter.

It only remains to add: they all lived happily ever after – and they did that.

Rhesus Negative Blood Group

The blood donor mobile service entered the yard. Like anything that broke the dullness of shipyard life, the event was a cause for celebration and was welcomed by the labour force.

The poster was pinned up in the painters' paint-shop and a group gathered round to read the information. Sammy Jones, the foreman painter, rushed out of his office at the corner of the department, brown dust coat flying behind him and his cigarette jerking to and fro in his mouth as he bellowed:

'Get to buggery, you lot! Get your paint and clear out! NOW!'

The painters shuffled back to their respective vessels, but the word spread like it does in any closed community: Donors were wanted.

Giving blood required that the donor left his ship and visited the mobile unit. This the painters did in droves, through no moral position, not even for the tea and biscuits.

I joined the other brothers of the brush and gave my pint. (Is it a pint? Or do folks just call it that?)

Later in the day, a nurse sought me out requesting my attendance, as I was blood group Rhesus Negative. I was in the paint-shop, topping up my paint pot when the nurse arrived. She informed me that I should sign up as a donor on a regular basis. Sammy rushed out in a foul temper, jabbing a finger at the nurse.

'Hey, you. Clear off! Don't keep my men from working. The lazy bastards only need an excuse.'

The nurse was aghast at Sammy's behaviour, not being aware that in the yards this sort of display was common practice.

'But… but…' the nurse stuttered. 'This man belongs to a rare blood type. He's Rhesus Negative and it's quite a special group.'

Sammy exploded. 'Special? Special? He's SPECIAL? What are we?' he said waving his hands to an invisible audience.

‘What are we? RUBBISH? Oh, no. He’s so special, his blood is special.’ Sammy had now gone completely berserk. ‘And we COMMONERS have only got the usual kind. But, oh, no, that’s not good enough for the likes of him. His has to be SPECIAL!’

The nurse looked at me in amazement. I shrugged and, giving a wan smile, felt it would be in my interest to be off and away to my boat at once.

The Field

Travelling widely in America, France and Italy my mate had photographed most of the local celebrations.

Barn building in Utah, the mardi gras, fetes, fiestas; he had participated in them all. 'It's the only way to get to know people,' he always insisted. Extensive as his knowledge of popular cultural events was, there was one omission – he had never attended an Orange Walk in his home town of Glasgow. Being an old Hutchy Grammar schoolboy and now earning his coin as a lecturer in fine art, he deemed it somewhat beneath him in the World League table of culture.

I, on the other hand, thought that it was one of the city's more colourful happenings and as important as anything that took place in Venice or Viareggio and, as a cultural event being celebrated on the streets, must be supported and encouraged. Enough! I'll come clean. I'm a sucker for the Lambeg drum.

In my more enlightened periods, I can understand why the Tims (oops, sorry! People who don't follow the Protestant credo) are not over-joyed by drums banging out a triumphalist din through the streets of the city. Well, if they don't like it… no, kidding aside, if the sound is so loathsome, why do Republican bands ape the drum-fife format?

At my instigation, it was agreed that this Saturday, instead of climbing the Buachaille Etive Mor, Stevie and I would sample the Walk or, to put it in its historical context, we would participate in celebrating the victory of protestant King William over catholic James II at the Battle of the Boyne in sixteen hundred and ninety.

On arriving at the public park, that was the 'Boyne' for the day, the first thing that one noticed was the sheer amount of litter. This is, in no way, to take to task the brothers and sisters of the L.O.L.S. (Loyal Orange Lodges Scotland), it was just evidence of their eating habits. They never wilfully threw away the wrapping paper from their hamburgers, but rather they just let the paper drift from their hands. Consequently, the park was reminiscent of a Christmas card, albeit with greasy snow. Various groups were assembled under colourful banners depicting long-forgotten events painted in what Stevie defined as 'folk art'. Many of the scenes were of total abstainers, which was a bit of a contradiction as many of the arty lay in a comatose state. OK, fair do's, they had walked the best part of three miles from Blythswood Square to the park. Although many of us walk the same distance daily to work, try skipping the route in cheap, hard shoes in time to music. They belched and farted as they lay and, in truth, who wouldn't with bits of mad cows and greasy fried onions inside them. The men, and to be thruthful, many of the sisters sported tattoos of badly-drawn horses on which sat a man holding aloft what looked like a light-sabre. There was a lot of talk about Fenians, forefathers and something called 'yore'. We walked amongst these foot-soldiers for a spell, but I felt it was time to visit the sharp end. So we made for the red, white and blue-adorned platform where the high heid yins were delivering their traditional message of love. We moved into the middle of a tightly-packed crowd of predominantly old men with unsmiling faces. Well, would you smile if you had to wear welders' gloves and a silly bowler hat, as well as the aforementioned footwear.

A narrow-faced Minister was just beginning his stint at the mike. He began his dirge by asking the assembled brethren to bow their heads in prayer and join him in giving thanks to God for bestowing on us a Royal Family that was the envy of the World. He then began to name them starting with her gracious majesty Queen Elizabeth of Great Britain and Northern Ireland, Defender of the Faith, a beautiful woman who had courageously led this small island against the machinations of the Roman anti-Christ. He then moved on to the many merits of Prince Philip von Battenburg (I mean Mountbatten). Then he proceeded to name every single member of the Royal Family in its entirety. This is quite a feat as we have the largest of such families in existence, so he was at it for quite some time. Like a Wee Free rap of sorts, but without the excitement. This form of prayer is well-suited to humourless, wee, dour men from across the Sheuch. He had at last exhausted his list (I forget the exact moment, having drifted into the dreamtime just after 'The Duke of Kent, Master Mason, Royal Arch…, etc. and only returned to full consciousness when he was reeling off the younger members, and only then because he had difficulty remembering their names and had to be prompted by one of his team).

It had obviously become a shade tedious, as I could detect shuffling of feet around me and the interrupted snores of some of the gathering who were in danger of falling asleep. Then he peaked. He hit his forte. A real serious prayer; he embarked on this without really bringing the previous rant to any kind of conclusion, but this was obviously his game. This is what he had trained for. All those tedious hours, the years spent preaching in small, unheated, tin-roofed halls were paying off. He was 'on'. 'All is vanity' says the Book, but a man can be allowed a wee turn now and again, especially in the service of the great Architect.

You could almost hear the proverbial pin drop.

'Oh, mighty omnipotent all-knowing God' he intoned. 'All-seeing creator of the universe, thank you from the very depths of our hearts for sending us sinners your merciful adoring son Jesus. We unworthy wretched people do not deserve this bountiful gift.' He lowered his voice for effect. 'Gentle Jesus. Lamb of God. Man of Peace…'

Then it happened.

'Fuck the Pope' shouted one of the exalted listeners. After the initial shock, I looked round in the direction of the outburst. Maybe he was emotionally overcome by the sermon or – I'm not being bitchy, here – could the bottle that cheers that he cradled in his arms have been a contributing factor? Anyhow, it was a bit of a let-down for the Minister, who gave an embarrassed cough, being on a roll of sorts and this being a form of religious *coitus interruptus*.

He coughed again, before disappointedly throwing in the towel and returning deflated to his seat at the rear of the platform. (We've all been there, but usually on more secular occasions)

The mike was quickly grabbed by a more seasoned trouper. A battle-hardened, rabble-rousing politician from the streets of Belfast. He asked for a show of hands to demonstrate our solidarity with one or other of the Loyalist terror gangs operating in Ulster. Hands shot up skywards instantly. 'Triumph of the will' nothing, this lot needed no prompting.

Only two hands were not raised and in that instant, never mind the sectarian jokes and the jaunty music, we felt real mind-numbing fear. As the crowd looked our way, we understood the sheer terror that can be spawned by such narrow-minded, parochial hatred. My heart pounded as some of the gathering crowded a bit too close. Stevie, as always being 'well turned out' as they say, looked a bit like a media person and the fact that he carried a camera didn't help matters. We could hear the word 'reporter' being muttered under a few breaths. We, as the tabloids say, made our apologies and left. We did so with a bit of alacrity, as the followers of the 'gentle Jesus, Lamb of God' were visibly upset.

Through the bandsmen we moved, one of whom was impressing his Union-Jacked girlfriend with a rendition on the flute of Liam Gallagher's latest. She was so obviously in love with the young flautist that she was oblivious to the grease from her hamburger dripping the front of her dress, upon which printed, in a circle at the centre over the national flag, was a portrait of the Queen. H.R.H. was now the recipient of a substance she would never have tasted and would never have believed was the food choice of nearly 100% of her loyal subjects.

The young man was as unaware of this as his young admirer. Whether many years from that day, when they have been a couple for a long period, he will still be as unaware, who can tell? Love, they say, is blind. So I wish the young Orange couple many years of happiness together. It's only fair.

We made our way to Stevie's car. After he relaxed being in unfamiliar surroundings he said:

'Back there, I thought I would be eating my camera!'

I laughed. He can always capture the moment with a neat phrase.

I reached over to play the cassette in the car.

Boom! Boom! Boom! The familiar notes of a song about a piece of old apparel that once belonged to the singer's father… and oh, yes, that 'yore' again.

Stevie pulled a face and switched off the music. Funny, for all his impeccable credentials, I always suspected he was 'wan o' them'. Maybe one of his family way back had jumped the dyke. Who knows? Who cares? But next Saturday we'll be climbing in Glencoe – it's less dangerous.

As we drove away from the park my foot was tapping silently. I could hear *that* tune. You can take the man out of the ghetto, but…

The Scotsman, Irishman, Londoner and Australian

The clerk held up a form and, not bothering to look up, addressed us. 'Us' being the line of unemployed crowding round his desk in the dole office. It had been a long morning; he was tired and just wanted a pint on his way home for lunch. But first he had one final task and he was in a hurry to get it completed.

'Two stickers' he announced.

A few men moved and one enquired if the job included painters. The clerk shook his head: 'Only paper-hangers.'

'I'm your man' shouted a man at the back of the group in a strong Cork City accent. 'I can stick with the best of them.'

'I'm a sticker, too' I declared, before anyone else responded. 'And I'm time-served with a full apprenticeship behind me' I added.

The Irishman had now moved to the front of the desk beside me: 'Just like me!'

The clerk glanced at the clock, closed his cabinet, and handed over the form. The Irishman grabbed it.

'Known each other long?' the clerk enquired.

'Way back. Man and boy, sir' said my new mate. He looked at the form: 'This address is over Belgravia way.'

'So?' said the clerk.

'Well, how do you expect two poor muckers to get there? If we walk and we arrive late the guv'nor will have us down as a pair of bad time-keepers and we don't want that now, do we? It would look bad on the person who gave us the form. And another thing…'

He was interrupted in mid spell by the clerk unlocking the cabinet and handing over a couple of notes.

'Thank you, sir. Fair play to you and we'll be away from your presence and I hope you and your good lady have a nice evening. You deserve it.'

With that we left the building.

'I'm Bob' I said.

'Dermott Declan Scanlon. And I'm dying with the thirst, so first thing is to find a nice hostelry.'

'But the job' I snapped.

'It'll keep. First things first, I always say' he answered.

Sullenly, I walked beside him, in silence. It didn't seem right somehow not to get to the address on the form. We entered a nondescript pub; the first and nearest.

'What's it to be, Jock?'

'Nothing. And it's not Jock'

'Bejesus, one of them is it? OK Bob, should I address you as Robert? For my part it can be anything, including Paddy, but that's only if it's accompanied by a drink. So that's settled then, Robert. It has a serious ring to it. Well, young Robert, when did you give up the hard stuff?'

'I've never touched it and can we get going now?'

'In good time, matey. In good time. A drink with friends shouldn't be rushed. Drinking is a social activity and is a thing to be treasured.'

He got to his feet, but indicated for me to remain seated.

'I'll just have another and then we're off.'

'Give me the address and I'll go myself' I said angrily.

He reached inside his jacket, handed over the form, then snatched it back, glanced at it and declared it was only round the corner; minutes away, in fact.

'Are you sure I can't tempt you Jock, er, Robert?'

'No. And if it's round the corner, I'm on my way.'

He gulped down his pint and stated that being rushed was a thing he detested, even worse than drinking alone.

'Right, what are you hanging about for Bob, Jock, Robert? To horse.' With that, he placed his glass down and marched off. I followed.

It was London in the 'swinging Sixties', but there wasn't much swinging for me and the thousands of my fellow countrymen down in the smoke trying to make our fortunes. Stories there were aplenty of this or that one finding that job that struck gold, so I was keen to get started on my quest and here I was hitting the rocks before I had a head of steam up.

As usual, in the building industry when new guys mate up they do a quick background check on each other. Who do you know? Where was your last job? Do you know Big Donegal? Wee Robbie from Caven? Glasgow Shug? Tam Scanlon from Neath? This is a form of self-protection, in case your new mate is in with the bosses and is helping to keep the blacklist up to date. With then crime of guilt by association being very much alive you could never be too careful.

I observed Scanlon closely. A painter with paint-spattered shoes was bad news – the sign of a careless worker. He was none of these things. Indeed, he was immaculate in a linen shirt, open at the collar, turned over his sports coat lapels in the old style. Immaculate, except everything was a size too big for him. Clean shaven, with a deeply-tanned face and when he laughed he displayed plenty of missing teeth.

'Excuse me' I said after we had walked a couple of blocks. 'Where is the job?'

'Oh, it's not a million miles from here, but keep marching, young Robert; when you're marching you're not fighting.'

'If it's a distance, let's take the bus, OK?'

'We can't. I spent the fare in the pub with you, so we'll just have to pace it out.'

'That wasn't your own money, then?'

'Dry your eyes. They always say Jocks are mean, but I've never found them so. No, never. Always stood their round and great mates when the going gets rough. Can it be Dermot-boy's bad luck to have landed up with a goody goody? Maybe my luck has run out.'

'What was your last job? Was it an easy number?' I enquired.

'No, Jocky. It was hard, in fact it was hard labour.'

'Where were you? Devil's Island?'

'No, I was a wild colonial boy doing hard labour in Australia.'

'A convict, eh?'

'Don't be coy, and you from North of the Border, too. Well, for your information, I was in jail, yes, but not for anything criminal.'

By arguing as we walked the distance went unnoticed and we found ourselves in front of an impressive building; thc type that most governments prefer in the game of one-upmanship that they practice with their official embassies.

He stopped and turned to me. 'You told your man back there that you were a sticker; well, you'd better be good, that's all.'

'What about you?'

'Man, I couldn't stick a moustache on a Halloween mask, but I thought I would bluff it for a while. Then you piped up with all that bull about serving your apprenticeship. You even convinced me. Yeah, we'll make a good team and no mistake.'

'Do you hang paper or not?' I demanded.

'Don't be so serious, man. Get with the programme. You hang the damn stuff and I'll paste. Right?'

We entered the building, which turned out to be the embassy of one of the newer African states. A giant of a black man got up from the chair where he had been dozing. The way all security men the world over do. He approached us.

'Jambo!' hailed Dermot and extended his hand. 'I am Dermot Declan Scanlon and this fine young man is Robert from Scotland. As you cannot fail to have noticed, I'm Irish and may I salute you for throwing out your colonial oppressors. We Irish did it first, of course, but welcome to the brotherhood of free nations.'

The fact that the country he was praising was now practising a barbaric form of repression equal to anything that their former masters dished out didn't seem to deter Dermot and he continued in this fashion, slagging the white man and damning him to Hell. The fact that we were white didn't seem to register with the security man, so good was the blarney the Irishman dished up. The guard led us through the lobby to where a building contractor was standing, studiously looking over a plan of the building. He looked up, then quickly glanced at his watch.

'You pair took your time getting here.' He fired off a whole list of clichés of the 'time is money, variety, which fell like burnt out fireworks at Dermot's feet.

'That traffic in old London Town is a killer' Dermot said by way of an answer. Then, attempting to look keen, he enquired where we were to start hanging the paper.

'Is there an architect on the job, or is it your good self that will be running the show?'

He indulged himself in a few clichés of his own, such as of the 'let's get this show on the road' kind. He rolled up his sleeves, having removed his jacket, which he placed neatly folded on top of a large wooden carved mask.

'Still you haven't answered me why it took so long to get here. Never mind that old traffic yarn.' The contractor was now looking us up and down.

'That dole didn't give us any cash to get here' Dermot lied. 'You'd of thought that it was his own money he was dishing out.' He turned to me: 'Don't hang about, Robert. Set up our paste table and let's get cracking.'

I set up the paste table, placed the step-ladders in position and picked up the rolls of wallpaper, ready for the off. We were under starter's orders, looking so efficient that the contractor smiled. Well, he didn't actually smile, but his face relaxed slightly and he told us he would now be off to do a bit of business elsewhere, but would look in on us in a couple of days' time to see our progress. As he neared the door, he turned and enquired if we had any questions.

'That there is, Sir. Would it be at all possible to have an advance, a sub like, to tide us over until pay day?'

As the contractor produced a bundle of notes from a roll he had in his jacket pocket, Dermot kept up a flow of patter.

'Congratulations are in order for young Robert here. He has just won the Society's gold medal for craft efficiency and you're lucky he has chosen to come here, having turned down an overseas posting with the

Crown.'

The contractor picked up a drawing, measuring tape, shade card and the other props that fool the customer and without replying, or even acknowledging the security man, he left.

'No expenses? Gold medal? What are you on about, mate?

'It's all show, Glasgow, all show. You'll find out on life's journey that the old bullshit baffles brains every time and gives you a bit of an edge.'

We got down to the business in hand and, possibly owing to the adrenaline coursing through my body, I papered fast and we finished our first room in a good time. We moved on to the next and in all this Dermot kept up a continual flow of banter: some good; some banal. All delivered in that unique Cork City accent. Working, at last, I relaxed and took stock of the job in hand.

'Slow down, boyo. You'll have us back in that dole queue. The quicker you do your stuff, the faster we'll be joining the reserve army of labour and we can't be having that now, can we?'

Inwardly, I was thinking that if the contractor returned and saw how I was performing he might transfer me to another site or, better still, offer me a permanent position. A long shot, but maybe someone in the embassy would arrange for me to be employed back in Africa. But I kept these thoughts to myself and just replied in a matter-of-fact way.

'Sounds reasonable.'

We worked in silence for some time, which was a relief from the torrent of banter overload. Silence was broken by Dermot suddenly blurting out his scheme.

London in that period was booming and the construction industry especially so. A scam was in operation throughout the city where there was a practice of adding names to the list of workers on a site – ghost workers – and dividing their wages among the labour force. The employers, for their part, also added names to the payroll, as many tenders were budgeted by the number of bodies on the site. This racket was widespread and known to all with a wink to officialdom.

'Why don't we claim for a third man? The job can stand it and the speed we're getting through it even justifies it.' Without waiting for my contribution, he continued.

'We can share the money between us.'

'Like the expenses from the dole office?' I interrupted.

'No, no. We weren't friends then, Bob.'

'Oh, and we are now?' I spat out.

'I'll phone the contractor right now and say we've taken the liberty of starting another man... Cuthbert. Yes, Cuthbert will help us finish the contract in record time.'

Laughing, he rushed off to phone. On his return, with the smile still in place, I knew his plan had succeeded and Cuthbert was now a member of our team. The remainder of the day was uneventful and I continued papering. When we finished for the day and I went home. He, of course, went to the nearest pub.

The following day we started promptly at eight and it was a lot easier now that there were three of us. The contractor looked in and although Dermot's head was banging he had enough blarney for the explanation of why we needed a third man. As always he went the extra mile and sung Cuthbert's praises.

'What a find he is' he nodded in the direction of nowhere specific, as if to indicate where Cuthbert was working.

'Well, where is he?' demanded the contractor.

'Oh, I forgot. Wee Jock there sent him for that new fast paste that he likes. Those gold medal boys are something else.'

Not entirely satisfied the contractor left.

After a few minutes had passed, Dermot commanded me to remove my overalls and join him in the nearest pub.

'We're a grand team and no mistake, eh? But that Cuthbert is a bit of a lazy bastard'

Even I laughed. Life is OK, I thought.

Now seated in the nearest pub – me with a ginger beer, him with a large whisky and a pint of Guinness – he told me his story. Yes, he had done time in Australia and it had been hard labour. He gulped down the spirits, licked his lips, and then slowly began his tale.

'I'd been working down under, on one thing or another, chasing the big bucks. I was on the Snowy Mountain hydro scheme. Mother of God that was a hard old station. I'd gone to Aussie chasing Margaret, the love of my life. We'd met in this very town, then it was full of boys and girls from over there. Big Aussies working on Airfields and dams, us city boys in the building trades. We would all meet in this place up Camden way and, sure, it was home from home. Margaret and me we would do all the things young folk do, all kinds of malarkey. Oh, we had fun. Then one day she announces she's going to Aussie land. My world came crashing all around me. I couldn't think straight. She was off without any discussion. No explanation. Nothing. I followed her after a few months and for ten years we were an item.'

He made that daft hand gesture that signifies quotation marks.

'Well, off and on, that is. What with me racing around all over the place, and the drink, she finally chucked me up and married this bloke from Wales. Not your *New South* Wales, mind, but bloody Wales. Man, your actual Cardiff, Wales. I was devastated and went on the sauce big time. For ages I begged, stole, never hurt anyone though, for the drink. I don't know where in that land I travelled. It's all a bit hazy, but the years went by and I never noticed, until one day that old home-sickness struck.

'I had always thought it was a bit of a cop-out; you know, if you couldn't make it, kind of thing. I was sitting in a dump of a bar when I heard a voice singing *The Boys of Wexford* and, in an instant, I knew I had to return to the UK. Funny that. I wasn't pining for the old country, but London city and all my old mates. So there and then I got my few things together and set off towards I knew not where. I met this old drover – well-read, old-school – and mated up for a while. He divulged the secret of the means to leave Australia.

'I managed to keep sober for a few weeks; slept rough to save my wages and bought myself a gallon of white emulsion and a throwaway brush. Then I put the drover's plan into operation. I wandered into a bourgeois suburb, picked out a busy road, opened my tin and proceeded to write:

'COMMUNISM FOR AUSTRALIA NOW!' and 'REVOLUTION NOW!'

'I painted on the hot tarmac as many revolutionary slogans as I could remember from my days arguing with the boys from the Connolly Association. I worked until the paint gave out, and then waited for the result. I had just finished "Arise Aus...", when the police arrested me. So far, so good. I had even begun to enjoy my slogans and my inherent sign-writing skills and was annoyed to be unable to finish my graffiti. "Come along now, Blue" the copper said. I aimed the paintbrush at him and although nearly dry the brush grazed his uniform and left a white stain.

"That's quite enough from you, mate" the policeman said as he put my arm up my back and took me to the station. What followed was an exercise in state repression. In the cell, I was punched silly by the copper's pals as he attempted to remove the residue of paint from his uniform. Being unsuccessful, he entered my cell and, in a rage, delivered the *coup de grace*. It was goodnight Vienna, Robbie.'

'Did you get tried?' I wanted more; it was a good story and was being well-told by a true spieler. He signalled for me to be patient, took a sip of Guinness and then continued.

'In the morning they dragged me to court, all the time giving me sly digs in the ribs and slagging off the Irish. I had enough balls to reply that they were probably descended from Irish convicts and prostitutes. The Judge sentenced me to six month's hard labour, with the proviso that I be deported on completion of my sentence. Mentally I thanked the old drover.'

I interrupted: 'Why doesn't everyone do the same thing? It seems an easy way to get home if things don't work out for you.'

He laughed. 'Easy? Oh, Robert, you're a raw one right enough. Hard labour is what it says on the tin, only more so. Easy? Easy?' he sniffed in derision. 'I never touched so much as a drop from the moment the cop grabbed me 'til they threw me on the boat four months later.'

'Four months, eh? You said six.'

'Two off for good behaviour and for being the hardest worker in the place, plus the fact that I painted the Guv'nor's house. We cleared an area of the bush where they are going to mine for uranium. We worked from dawn to way by dusk, as the crafty bastards had rigged up lights, powered by a genny. Paddy, at one point, thought he'd have to top himself, but it cleaned me up. When they put me on that ship I was as fit as I'd ever been in my life. The Captain, one of yours, Rob, was given the paperwork to sign, then we set sail. He was a big shirt-lifter.'

'Gay' I interjected, 'Gay!'

'Gay? No, not him. Not a bit of it. A big moaning old sea-dog poofter. I was billeted in a locker-space near to his cabin and it gave the crew no end of mirth watching me fend him off after he'd had his nightcap of Scotch. I refrained from participating and had to listen to their inane slagging.'

'But how come you're here and not back in Cork?'

'That's easy. I jumped in Rotterdam and made my own travel arrangements. I took the big man's clothes; smart stuff, but, as you can see, a bit too large for me.'

'A thief as well' I said.

'Cool, brother. Be cool. It's only the craic. Anyhow, finish your wee ginger beer and let's be getting back.'

The contractor was at the entrance. Fuming.

'Where have you pair of idle bastards been? The only one working is Cuthbert, if you follow my drift.'

We did follow his drift and, after knuckling down to a severe day's work, we knew the incident would be forgotten.

Room after room, after room we papered and were on a roll of high performance when bad luck struck. Dermot had won some money at the dogs and gone on the piss big time. He now became a passenger and sat on a chair as I pasted, papered, moved steps and everything myself. He was a complete liability. He sat and muttered to himself and the word

Margaret was a constant. Tears trailed his face. He got up and went to the door and never returned.

The job completed, I went to the contractor for my wages.

'I'll take Cuthbert's, as well' I announced, feeling smart that I had put one over on a Londoner.

'Sure thing' he said. 'No problem. You all done really well. As a matter of fact I priced the embassy for ten Cuthberts; and they came across.'

'Any sign of Mr Scanlon? I enquired.

'No, but he phoned in sick, and insisted all his money goes to some Margaret in Australia.'

The Journey

He often did this now he had endless hours to fill. 'This' being the buying of an all-day run-around bus ticket. It was a bit like mainland Europe café society, where the regulars sit in the sun with their coffee people-watching. There was no coffee and very little sun, but the people-watching was every bit as interesting and, of late, it had become his obsession.

He sat where he always did; in the centre at the back of the bus. This gave him the optimum position in which to view his fellow passengers. Like a punter in the betting shop who studies the form of the horse, weather, distance and times. He chose his routes with the same fastidiousness.

He had his favourite routes and days and if the passengers didn't, for whatever reasons, play their parts, he would get off and get on to another bus. On many occasions he had been known to return the way he had just come in order to facilitate a happening.

No need for such action today. He had only been on the bus moments when he knew this journey was going to be a good one. The diversity of people always fascinated him and he did not have long to wait before he sat up and took interest.

Noisily clambering aboard, pushing and shoving, were five thin, pale spotty young men in an assortment of athletic clothing, tops and tracksuits, with famous sporting names printed on them. The incongruity of their dress and the general unfitnessness of the group made our traveller laugh quietly to himself. As they laughed, which they did almost continually when one of the group made a monosyllabic remark, he noticed how bad and ill-looked after were their teeth. A few had teeth missing, whether from neglect or through fighting he could only guess, but as one of the group had a much-scarred face, he thought the latter. Even the scarring was of morbid interest. The young man had fresh scars crossing his face from the opposite direction that his previous semi-faded ones did. His neck was also criss-crossed with razor marks. This gave him a horribly comical appearance.

When they had got onto the bus, the youths were puffing and blowing, out of breath, after having had to move marginally faster than normal. This was a peculiar thing about the city. Once, men walked around in a brisk manner with a prize-fighter's gait; then, overnight, it was the aluminium walking stick and they were old. No in-between stage. Young. Bang! Old.

He was intrigued. Having been the recipient of the cod liver oil and the orange juice, he was in better all-round shape than these young men and, although he shouldn't have, he felt superior and allowed himself a flicker of a smile.

They were still at it, braying and jabbing each other. When the bus jerked to a stop this threw a couple of young men into each other and was the cause for more inane laughter.

The bus had stopped to pick up a young mother. She struggled to climb aboard with her small baby in one arm and her half-folded pram in the other. She awkwardly fumbled in her pocket for the fare, while attempting to put the pram in the place provided. All this she performed without disturbing her baby, which she held secure to her breast. The task was proving difficult and she looked pleadingly at the young men for assistance; none came. What did come her way was a remark from one of them, which caused another outburst of laughter. She flashed the boy a defiant look, then lifted the pram and put it on the ledge. She was conscious that the entire bus was watching her and she sucked in her blushing cheeks and turned her attention to the baby.

She was very young. Indeed, she had only recently left her own childhood and her behaviour was, in many ways, childish. She fussed with the baby's outfit very much like a child playing with a doll and acted her role as she had copied it from some daytime television programme.

Two elderly, white-haired women put their heads together and whispered something about the young mother. They nodded their heads reproachfully and continued to stare at the girl. They both pursed their lips, reminding him of a cat's arse! Not much of that milk of human kindness on tap.

The girl was sitting near the young men and one put a pale, thin arm over her shoulder in some private joke for his mates. She blushed again, on observing him, and brusquely pushed his arm away. It was strange, thought our traveller, that not that long ago she had probably laid out her stall to catch a young man not too dissimilar to her tormentors.

There was no way of knowing how the girl perceived herself. She had on a light nylon blouson, pink in colour with a dried milk stain where her baby nestled her head. She maybe didn't clean it off on purpose; it was a badge of honour in her peer group, he concluded. On her tiny hands she wore an assortment of gold rings, one on every finger and even one on her thumbs. The same gold spelled out her name – Kimberley – hung on a gold chain around her neck. Her hair was tied back with a rubber band in pony-tail style.

He felt a deep sadness for the girl, but it was possibly not what the girl was experiencing. He could be one-hundred-per-cent wrong. That was what made this people-watching game interesting. It was not an exact science. It was all conjecture and that was all it could ever be, but he, now and then, in a kind of psychological way, believed he got near enough the truth.

When the girl-mother got off the bus, again without any assistance from the young men, he felt it was one of those times. There was a lull in the men's babble, then one of them passed what must have been a ribald remark and this was followed by an outburst of guffaws. It showed neither joy nor malice but as the bus drew away his eyes fixed on the mother and baby. It seemed to speak louder than words to our psychologist.

Eventually, the young men disembarked and our traveller had nothing more interesting to do than fold and re-fold his ticket. The bus was passing through a dull part of the city. Once, this section had been of great architectural interest, but successions of philistine 'representatives' of the people had, in their inspirational acumen, had them pulled down; to be replaced with 'machines for living', which didn't hold anyone's attention for more than the briefest of moments.

He had, absent-mindedly, made so many shapes with his bus-around ticket that it no longer resembled its original form and would be worthless if the inspector came on board. He was in the process of putting it in his pocket, out of the way of his bored hands, when she came on.

What a character. Even in the first few seconds of her coming aboard he knew she was the best 'specimen' he had seen in a very long time.

With much audible sighing and bronchial wheezing, she perched herself on that single seat at the front of the bus. It was raised higher than all the others and it was positioned in such a way that whoever occupied the seat was automatically on show for the judgement of their fellow-travellers. It took a special kind of courage to sit there and he could only marvel at the woman's bravery as she displayed nearly every defect that it's possible to have inflicted on one person. As the ticket-folding was now over, he could give her his absolute concentration and he did. She leaned forward in the seat and gravity pulled all of her loose parts downwards. They all wobbled in harmony with the vehicle, but the various parts - breasts, chins, belly – all wobbled in different directions. He was fascinated. She had an inelegant face with bruised, swollen lips that had been painted the brightest red. When she coughed, what teeth she still had were displayed, large, yellow and, here and there, stained with the red lipstick. Her broken nose had a glittering stud embedded on one side, which only drew attention to how off the true it was. Her crowning glory was a ferocious shiny black wig, except for the roots, which were very white. It stuck out in all directions, stiffened with lacquer. She held her fat, podgy hands on her lap. The nails, which were broken, were painted the same shade as her lips, and she wore a very small gold watch on a thin light strap. It looked as if some lucky charms hung from the strap, but he was too far away to be certain.

Her ample body, which she had squeezed into the seat, was covered in a thick Arran-style, off-white, woollen cardigan. It hung down, out of shape owing to both side pockets being full of heavy objects. He guessed, by her nicotined fingers, that one of the pockets contained her cigarettes and lighter. There was a handkerchief also, of the kind that snuff-takers use. Our man had only ever seen them in Liverpool, but that was years ago.

Periodically, he exchanged glances with others aboard, and he noticed one or two people near to the woman had expressions on their faces denoting a foul smell from her direction.

The two white-haired women continually looked around the vehicle and made tutting noises and shook their heads at anyone who returned their glance. Well, that pair didn't likc the young mother, now they were looking disapprovingly at someone nearer their age, he noted. They both were smartly dressed, with neat silk scarves over their shoulders and under their hats tight white curls were visible. Their glasses flashed as they looked this way and that. They were as clean as the woman was not, but he just knew what they valued – and it wasn't humanity.

He shrugged; they were someone's mothers, wives even. He returned to the woman. She was now putting her legs together and sticking them out in front of her. The filthy feet had the same shade of varnish and round the fat ankle nearest his viewpoint he could make out a thin gold chain. She replaced them on the floor the better to give purchase to a bout of coughing. Not once did she cover up her mouth.

The bus was now in a less prosperous part of the city. An old, frail-looking man was attempting to climb the steps. He carried in the crook of his arms his walking sticks and, just like the young mother earlier, his eyes searched the vehicle for help. Our man prepared to go to the aid of the old man, but he was beaten to the draw. She was on her feet at once, and taking the walking sticks in one swollen hand, she lifted the frail man on board. She waved the driver away when he demanded to see the man's pass, and led him to a seat. He was breathless with the effort, but mumbled his thanks to the woman. She held his sticks as he grasped the rail for support. Even from the back of the bus our man could see his veins in the parchment-white hands. His shirt cuffs and jacket were shiny with age and neglect, but he had made the effort to put on a tie.

At one point, the man stood up shakily, but as it coincided with the driver applying his brakes, he fell over having such a weak grip on the bar. The woman picked him up. Well she was the nearest, our observer said to himself, but he knew it to be a lie. Other passengers made small movements as if they were about to help too. Liars all. Why do we act like this, he thought. Why can't we just do these things, help others? Is it embarrassment? Or what?

She comforted the frail old man with reassuring utterances. When the bus approached one of the city's famous hospitals she assisted him off the bus gently and then proceeded to slowly walk him up the road to the entrance. She was not doing it for any gain whatsoever. One look at the man's vacant, confused state made that clear.

The bus was now quite quiet. The two tight-curled ladies stared straight ahead. The silence was broken by a woman sitting by herself. She spoke up: 'I feel so ashamed. That woman has shamed us all… no excuses… we deserve to get cancer!'

He knew it to be true. He put his hand in his pocket and resumed ticket-folding. He didn't want to be part of this. When he thought a suitable time had passed he moved to the front of the bus and got off.

He was glad now that the bus was out of his line of vision. With moist eyes, he looked at the folded ticket crumpled into a ball. He took a deep breath, looked round at the busy street, and then made his way towards the bus stop.

Jimmy The Barber

We remained behind in the school hall long after the Friday night meeting of the Boys' Brigade. The reason was that two of the 'local poofs' were on the prowl outside and were waiting for a 'capture'.

This was years before the changes in the sexual climate and I can still recall the horror in which we thought of 'being taken away by a strange man'. Even yet I still sometimes feel, if only for a millionth of a second, the apprehension and fear of those days.

We lived in the Maryhill district of Glasgow; with its famous barracks, home of the legendary Highland Light Infantry. So we were no strangers to the stories told and re-told about what some of the regiment did for money with the 'poofs' and the horrific yarns of what the squaddies then dished out in the way of a thank you.

The date is difficult to pinpoint exactly, but our two 'friends' outside were dressed in the style of the times. John, the quiet one, was wearing a dark blazer with an R.A.F. emblem in gilt thread on the breast pocket. Jimmy the Barber, being the more adventurous of the pair, was wearing his trousers a 'half-mast', showing off about three inches of his bright canary-yellow socks. He also wore a matching scarf and, to top it all, sported what we called his trade mark: rimless spectacles of the Glenn Miller type.

Both had on the shoes of the period: giant crepe-soled objects, popularly called 'brothel creepers'. Considering their sexual bias, that somehow didn't seem to fit.

Why were we frightened of Jimmy, then?

A few months previously I had experienced a dreadful few minutes when the older boys grabbed me as Jimmy was passing and removed my snake-belt, then my pants. They called out to Jimmy that they had a nice boy for him and, to the tune of La Donna Mobile, some of them sang:

'Young boys are cheap today.

Cheaper than yesterday.'

The Barber just kept on walking, but, in my predicament, I didn't notice; so when the boys freed me, having become bored with the game, I burned with anger and humiliation. I thought of a million horrible things I would do to Jimmy when I became a man.

I should mention that the youths who were holding me were only a few years older than me, but were light years ahead in experiences, as all of them were at that time in the Merchant Navy and acted older than their years. On many a wet, damp Glasgow evening with nothing to do and nowhere to go my pals and I would stand in a shop doorway at the street corner and listen to these latter day Marco Polos, as they competed with one another in outrageous story-telling. They would all try and top each other with yarns of the exotic things that they had seen; the fabulous brothels they had visited; the strange practices they had seen or had taken part in. All this was exciting to us younger boys and our eyes opened wider, literally, with each story, as our heads ached with trying to come to terms with it all. These ancient mariners would act out their stories using colourful seamen's slang, adding in a sprinkling of Arab phrases to give the tales authenticity. We would roar with laughter at the way they broke into their version of Pidgin English, with cries of:

'You want my leetle seester, Johnny?' and ' You likey very much Johnny Spanish Fly for the reluctant maidens?'

It was an education to us and we would all laugh heartily, while we were all in the warmth and safety of the collective. But on leaving the corner and returning home alone our minds quickly became the receptacles of all kinds of fears; the uppermost being, what if Jimmy the Barber should be waiting round the next corner.

At the top of the street corner, near the tenement I lived in, was the Forth and Clyde canal. A wonder of the industrial world when built, and a busy stretch of water in its heyday, but by the period of which I'm writing, it was in a very neglected and sad state. Boys were warned by their parents not to go near it, because if they fell in to the deep dark water they would lose their lives. Girls were taught that they would lose something far more valuable and, under these circumstances the canal was a place to be avoided. Avoided that is except for Jimmy and his pal, as this was the area where they would bring their 'captures who, after rendering a service, were given half-a-crown. They used to tell the boys that the reason behind it all was that in the evening they were going out with their girlfriends and didn't want to risk 'putting them in the club'; so they preferred to be, as they put it, 'emptied out'. This seemed plausible to the boys, as they had only recently found out from their pals in the Merchant Navy where babies did come from. We had no wish to join the boys who had been of help to the two men. It made us a bit squeamish to think of it. This was uppermost in our minds as we made our plans to leave the school hall by our different ways and make a run for it.

The years have passed and my ex-Brigade mate and I have worked at a variety of occupations, both here and abroad, and have collected our own tales. Indeed, he followed the advice of the street-corner lawyers and joined the Merchant Navy. All this has heightened our tolerance threshold. Nowadays, we don't believe one per cent of the stories told by old soldiers, and that also applies to the punters who bring the basics to our shores. We are more tolerant of people with different sexual beliefs, as we know that nobody fits perfectly into the pigeon-hole marked 'normal'. Being men of the world, we subscribe to the 'live and let live' code. No longer do we think of homosexual men as queers and people to be afraid of. But...

A few months back, we were having a quiet drink in a pub, off the beaten track to avoid the usual action-replay of the meeting we'd just left, when into the pub walked a wee old man, with rimless Glenn Miller spectacles.

In a flash the years rolled back – livc and let live, be damned. I felt the colour drain from my cheeks and my legs go weak. The urge to bolt for the door was very strong indeed; one doesn't need to be an amateur student of Pavlov to appreciate the anxiety I was experiencing. I looked over the table at my mate, who, catching my eye, looked round at the old man. He almost spluttered his beer over me as he blurted out: 'Fuck me, it's Jimmy the Barber!'

We both laughed simultaneously, with maybe just a trace of nervousness, recalling the time many years ago when two small boys had planned to make a run for it from a school hall to escape from this wee man and his pal.

A Night to Remember

It was a dark autumn evening. My sister and I were part of a group of other young children making our way to a corrugated tin hut which belonged to one of the many religious groups which flourished in the city all those years ago. We were going to the Band of Hope. This was a temperance movement attempting to combat drunkenness – they had their work cut out. Of that, there was no dubiety.

We kids had just celebrated hallowe'en and in the hiatus before Christmas fever gripped us, it was a place to go on a Friday evening. Back then there wasn't the money or choices that exist today – really it was the only show in town.

There we would be subjected to lectures on the evils of strong drink by sober suited ex-drinkers turned fervent abstainers. Nothing wrong with that of course, but the movement's presentations hadn't kept up with the times. For instance, a wall poster depicting a decrepit man lying in the gutter bore the caption 'Once I built airships, before I succumbed to the demon drink'. Another showed a drunk squatting outside a hut. In a thought bubble was drawn a brawny smiling blacksmith. 'I was strong enough to shoe hundreds of cavalry horses, but I wasn't strong enough to fight strong drink'. Even then I thought they were a bit melodramatic, but I enjoyed studying the drawings as I listened to the speakers.

We all sat through the rants of the abstainers for two reasons. One was for the sticky bun that each child was given, and the other was the lantern slide show.

The slides were truly dire and, like the posters, were from a bygone age and the garb of the protagonists would have been easily recognised by our grandparents. Featured on the slides would be ragged children of about our age tugging in vain at their father's sleeves, tearfully attempting to drag him home to where, in the next slide, his prematurely aged wife sat with her face in a Paisley shawl. The father is still in his working clothes, indicating that he has gone on the booze straight from work and has done in the wages.

This stuff we sat silently through, wide-eyed with our clasped hands and all of our feet swinging from the wooden bench. When the slideshow was over and the house lights came on we would all start talking at the same time and order had to be brought to the meeting by one of the sober old blokes in attendance.

He, like the other grown-ups, was not only sober in matters relating to alcohol but his choice of suits and general behaviour. We were all far too young to appreciate the stresses and pressures that those men running the meeting were experiencing. Our own dads, in comparison, when drunk would be boisterous and childlike and we would be infected with their joyfulness.

The sober men would take it in turns to tell us tales of the horrendous effects of drink on their lives. Sad as many of those stories were, I loved them, being a sucker for a good yarn, and I looked forward to hearing them.

Then it was the singing section. The songs were always of a quasi-sacred type sung by other adults with utter conviction.

'I'll walk with God,' a woman was singing. This puzzled me, even as a child, because I regularly saw her walking with great difficulty, not with God but with her wee husband, who also had a bit of difficultly walking as they were thrown out of the Caber Feidh at closing time.

It was now the turn of us children to chant the mantra of the organisation. Strange that I can still remember it down all the years, when I struggle with the nine times table. We loudly proclaimed:

'I promise here by grace divine
To drink no spirits ale or wine
Nor will I buy nor sell or give
Strong drink to others
While I live
This my solemn resolve shall be
No drink! No drink! No drink – for me'

The last line we roared with fervour. Some of my mates say that some of the sentiments are still with me today. Especially the parts relating to not buying or giving strong drinks to others – this usually comes back to me when it's my round; proving the truth of the Jesuit's claim about the first seven years.

Next song on the agenda was our second best favourite – 'Mycupisfullandrunningover'. This was accompanied with gestures that I saw years later on Top of the Pops. Then we were straight into our No. 1 favourite, 'Jesusbidsusshine'. When the last chord died away we clapped with glee – it was sticky bun time. This was served with small 'Shipman's paste' glasses of 'soft drink' as the grown-ups emphasised. We kids called it ginger – except that we drunk every flavour except ginger. The lurid colours of the drink were more than welcome in our otherwise austere world.

'Chunky' sat with us children. He was a grown up but different from the other dark-suited team. He wore a red fez. Whether it came from an uncle at El Alamein or from his work with the cleansing department, we never found out. The 'Clennie', like the lamp-lighting department, carried a disproportionate number of, well let's be humane, underachievers. Nowadays you need a box full of O's A's, Highers and a PhD to get an interview for such a career.

Chunky was a happy individual, always smiling. He had none of the deviousness we associated with the adults from the real world. He was from their world, but he had kept a childishness and a sense of fun about him. We kids loved him. We didn't know about role models then, but if we had and a snap poll had been taken, I'm certain all of us, girls as well as boys, would have wanted to be like him.

The meeting had almost run its course. The janitor was standing in the doorway, mop and pail in hand, waiting to start cleaning the hall. One of the sober suits glared at him and glanced at the wall clock. He was not going to be rushed, this was his show, and the real reason he didn't want the meeting to end was because he knew that as soon as the janitor had completed his task he would be heading to the 'Caber Feidh' to get a wee drink before it closed at 9.30pm; so to save the man from this terrible crime he asked if anyone in the audience hadn't yet sung, but wanted to come up to the podium. As he self-righteously adjusted his spectacles he was sated with satisfaction. Doing God's good work was, well, good. Suddenly Chunky was beside him.

Chunky held the fez with both hands, threw back his head and roared 'I'd rather have a paper doll to call my own'. Mr Sobersuit was flabbergasted. The janitor was convulsed with laughter. Us children cheered our champion. We knew he was genuine. We understood the song wasn't really sacred but it being sung with such truthfulness, we shared Chunky's love. He was singing with all his heart. What a night. Chunky – wherever you are – I raise my glass to you.

Salud!

The Jump

The stuntman ran to the edge of the roof then stopped abruptly. He shook his head, walked back to his starting mark. Again he set off along the tiled roof and again when he neared the edge, he hesitated. It was one of those days, we all have them, when nothing seems to work.

Rewind – a film was being made in the city and I was part of the construction squad. We had built two buildings about eighteen feet apart. The roofs had been constructed so that they sloped towards each other, slated and hosed down for maximum cinematic effect.

Stuntmen in the industry negotiate their fees based on the time and danger involved in what is required of them. Our man had made his deal over the phone without having seen the job and was now regretting it.

He wore the uniform of his craft. A black nylon jacket with his name printed on the front. On the back his nickname TIGER and a long list of films on which he has worked. It's a bit like the battle honours on regimental flags and serves the same purpose. No regiment has a blank flag so no stuntman has only one or two titles. He sat down and lighted a cigarette. A young runner brought him a plastic cup of coffee. He sipped it with a worried expression on his face. When he finished drinking he threw the last drops from the cup, crushed the cigarette underfoot and stood up. He then slowly paced out his steps from his mark to the edge of the roof. He counted aloud.

The jump had to take place the next day. He was distraught. He slowly approached where we were working.

'All right mates,' he opened with. 'Good job for you is it?' Mac, our construction manager, put down the plans he was studying. 'Aye, it's been fine so far. There's the usual headache, never enough time, but aye it's O.K.'.

I spoke up, 'How do you like it up here so far?'

'Yeah, great mate – really great. But I haven't seen too much of the place. I only flew in this morning and I'm booked on the return flight tomorrow.'

'Aye, that's too bad, you could have joined us for a bevvy tonight,' I replied.

The stuntman addressed Mac.

'Could I speak to you a minute Jock?' He indicated that they should both walk away. 'Fire ahead pal – there's no secrets between me and my squad.'

'Well it's a tiny bit delicate', said Tiger looking at the edge of the roof.

'Could you do me a big favour – a really big favour?'

'Go on', Mac said.

'You know I have to make the jump tomorrow – it's a crucial scene – no avoiding it. Well to be truthful I'm off my game – I can't put it together somehow. I've lost it. That's the worst of this racket. If I don't do the stunt within minutes someone will have phoned down south and I'll never get another job in the industry.'

'Jump the fucking thing then,' said one of our crew.

'Oh yeah I could do that, but I wouldn't promise that I would reach the other side'.

'So what's the favour?' Mac.

'Would it be possible to bring the buildings closer together? Somehow move the scaffolding? It's a long shot but if you lads could find a way to solve this I would be grateful. There would be a substantial drink in it for you'.

'Leave it with me Tiger – your problem's solved. The lads and I will work on the set after the wrap. When everyone has left we'll work on a few hours and move the building a couple of feet. It won't be noticeable to the grown-ups but we'll know and more to the point, you'll fly over the distance piss easy.'

'Would you do that?' the stuntman was smiling for the first time.

'Just one thing though', said Mac. 'Don't make it look too easy'.

'Cheers boys, I'm off to my hotel for an early night, I'm washed out'.

Next day the paraphernalia of filming was everywhere in evidence.

The camera crew with their butch mountaineering clothing calmly setting up shop. The director and his team perused the shooting script. The actors were discussing their respective mortgages. The stuntman winked at the construction crew.

We gave him the thumbs up. He swaggered around with this group, then that group, showing an interest in the mechanics of filmmaking. He was on nodding terms with many of the crew having worked together in the past. As he strutted around waiting his cue, he was very much the stuntman, cracking his knuckles noisily and doing loosening up exercises. Then he was on.

The first assistant called him to his mark. He nonchalantly took up his position and waited for the signal to do his thing.

The first assistant director silently signalled to him. He was off. A fast run to the edge and then he sailed through the air and landed dramatically on the other roof.

'Will I go again guv?' he enquired of the director.

'No, it was absolutely perfect, we've got it. Well done, you're wrapped Tiger. Good luck, see you around.'

The assembled crew applauded and then continued organising for the next scene.

The stuntman made his way down from the roof and in a few minutes had joined us where we were carrying out our work.

He shook us all warmly by the hand.

'Thanks lads nice one, I owe you'. Mac faced him.

'You don't owe us a thing mate. We had so much work to do last night we never got round to the thing we discussed'.

'Do what?' gasped the stuntman.

'I knew you could jump it – it was all in your head'.

The swagger went out of the stuntman's demeanour and beads of sweat appeared on his forehead. He was pale as he turned and dejectedly walked away from us.

'Look on the bright side mate – you did it,' I shouted to him.

'What was the alternative? Cheers', he shouted without looking back. 'I'll remember this town'.

It was Christmas Day...

Glasgow in the early Fifties. The country was slowly recovering from the aftermath of the war and was in the middle of a dull period of austerity. All the hopes and dreams of the populace had long since evaporated. There was a kind of resignation that life was just a long series of second prizes.

The events that were about to be played out were set in one of the city's old established restaurants.

The restaurant only closed for one day in the year – Christmas Day – and in that short period the entire place was cleaned, furniture moved and re-moved countless times and the entire establishment painted. The place consisted of the main restaurant, large smoking-room, kitchen, cloakroom and toilets. To execute the whole operation, a small army of painters was assembled by one of the many paint firms based in the town.

The painters stood outside Anstriker's early that Christmas morning waiting for the kick-off. No chance of seeing young Tommy open his presents. The presents had to be paid for; and by denying themselves most of life's pleasures they could just about manage it.

There was no Anstriker. The owner was the grandson of the family that had founded the restaurant in the 1890's and had the air of superiority that usually goes with inherited wealth. Having never strived nor struggled for anything in his life he was as distant from his grandparents as it was possible to be. He moved with ease through the crowd of workmen and put the key in the door. He turned to the diminutive foreman: 'Are we all fit?' he enquired. 'Up for the job in hand?'

'This day will be spoken of in years to come, Sir' cackled the foreman, who was a contradictory mixture of obsequiousness and firmness. 'Take it from me!'

The men all filed through the door. The owner, first of course, was already in switching on the lights with one hand and with the other deftly picking up his mail as he moved. He was followed by the foreman. Next came the ten 'regulars'; these were the painters who had been employed by the firm on a near continual basis. Then followed the three new-starts. As the name implies, they were men taken on for this job and, as such, knew neither each other nor the other men. Lastly, the three apprentices; two who were nearing completion of their five years' training and the youngest of the entire labour force, who was barely into the first six months of his apprenticeship.

The young boy was keen to learn all aspects of the painting and decoration craft, but much more than that he desperately wanted to be accepted into the world of working men.

He observed everything, absolutely everything. The smallest details he noted. He yearned to understand the way men related one to another and, if possible, discover the secrets that would make his journey through their world easier. He desperately wanted to be part of the tribe.

Once inside the restaurant, the foreman quickly set up what was termed the paintshop. This consisted of a folded dust sheet, spread out in an out-of-the-way corner, on which were placed the various types of paint, arrayed according to their function. Beside it stood the foreman and the young man. Standing in a line in front of the paintshop stood the painters, wearing a variety of protective clothing: white overalls, bib and brace, second-hand dentists' jackets and white tunics with brass buttons that had last seen action serving table aboard the White Star Line.

Every man had his sleeves rolled up above the elbow, indicating his readiness to participate in whatever was asked of him.

On their arms, alongside the usual religious tattoos, many were adorned with the insignia of famous Scottish regiments. They had all served in the forces during the war. Some had participated in battles that had been household names. Some were even heroes and had performed feats of outstanding bravery. They all stood with some trepidation facing the foreman.

He stood most of the time, hands on hips, head forward, and chin jutting out in a truculent fashion; so much like Sawdust Caesar. The owner was delighted to see that every so often he admonished a painter by holding up a finger and stabbing it at the man in front of him, bellowing out: 'None of your scamping, my lad. Three coats d'you hear. The full three coats.'

The owner would have been less delighted had he really known what was going on. The performance was all for his benefit and meant the exact opposite. The message that was actually being handed out was indicated by the stabbing finger – ONE coat and ONLY one coat – and it was a diktat.

As the apprentice handed each man a paint pot and brush the foreman gave out his instructions, such as the information that the sandpaper and dusting brush were in the paint. Unlike the wagging finger, these orders were delivered *sotto voce*. Each man understood what was being asked of him. It meant that he had to avoid sanding down anything and, instead of using a dusting brush, he was to mix the dust in with the paint and, in painters' terms, 'sweeten it off'.

Each operative was a time-served journeyman and a fully paid-up member of his craft union, which forbade such practices. Each man knew it to be wrong. Each man carried out the foreman's orders without a murmur. Jobs were impossible to find at the best of times and non-existent in winter.

The foreman stood barely five feet and was known throughout the industry as a hard task-master. He carried out his superior's orders without hesitation and if, by accident or design, the boss had displayed any leniency, he edited out. He lacked compassion or fairness and had no use for courtesies of any kind. He barked out his demands whenever he was forced to speak and even his 'good mornings' were reluctantly given, in a brusque manner. He had served the same employer, man and boy, and although a tyrant towards anyone he thought inferior to him, the change in behaviour in the other direction was sickening to observe. He would giggle like a child at any feeble joke and his fawning made Uriah Heep seem like a dangerous revolutionary.

Some said that the reason behind his behaviour was many years ago his son had been knocked down and killed and this had soured him. Work for him was a form of displacement therapy. Whatever the reason, he was a hard man. He picked the labour force and on his say so it was decided whether you worked all year or were laid off in the winter. Believe me, back then, that was awesome power and he knew it. Barely five feet? The man was a GIANT!

He directed his squad with a nod of the head towards the area he thought an individual could best apply himself.

In the main restaurant were positioned all the regulars, some of whom were now engaged in delicate decorative work on the ornate cornices. The new men were all in the toilets.

The two older apprentices were sent to the kitchen and the young boy was used as a gofer or runner; delivering paint in a large steel pail to wherever it was required. This prevented anyone leaving their post on any pretext whatsoever. No one must be idle for a moment. Consequently the young boy was soon red-faced and in a state of agitation running in all directions whenever one of the men shouted for him.

Owing to the shortness of time to complete the painting of the restaurant, all the fastest methods of execution were brought into play, like spirit paint. So fast drying, the painters said it could dry on a butcher's prick, whatever that meant. There was paint so loaded with a drying agent you had to be fast to complete the job at all, and the new-fangled emulsion paint that the old hands said would one day ruin the trade.

Looking up from his labours, the young apprentice saw in front of him a smiling woman. She had tight white curls and rimless glasses. Though her face was lined, she must be nearly ninety, thought the boy, it was kind. Aggie had been standing observing him for some time. She was smartly dressed in full waitress uniform: slim, black skirt; black top, with starched white collar and cuffs. On her head, held by a couple of pins, was a starched lace cap of sorts, bearing the name 'Anstriker'. She wore black nylons, with seams that ran up the back of her legs. These seams never departed from the true, not even by a millimetre. She had wide-fitting black court shoes. On her wrist was a small gold cocktail watch. A thick gold chain and locket were round her neck. The boy noted all this because she was immaculate.

She told him she had retired the day previously, but insisted on coming in on Christmas day to help out. She said that she had come to know some of the old painters over the years and anyhow it was the best way to spend Christmas.

The boy asked her why she was so turned out and they 'were only painters'.

'There's no such thing as 'only'. You're not 'only' anything' she snapped back. ' You're doing a job of work and should have respect for that.'

As she turned, she gave the boy a beautiful big smile. 'Always remember' she said, 'Only the *best* is good enough for the workers!'

The apprentice was beside himself with joy. Recently, he had joined the Young Communist League and taken to mouthing such slogans as: 'dialectical historical materialism', 'democratic centralism', 'development of the development' and other such inanities. But one slogan he thought was truly wonderful and she had just declared it:

'Only the best is good enough for the workers.'

He liked her chutzpah.

One of his duties took him to the kitchen to replenish the paint of the two older boys, who were coating the greasy wood with some ultra-fast-drying concoction. As they worked they were engaged in a banal game that entailed guessing film stars names by their initials only.

On entering the kitchen, the boy observed that Edmund was not taking it sportingly that his initials 'M.M.' were not being accepted.

'Everyone knows that M.M. stands for Marilyn Monroe' he muttered. He attempted to rope in the young boy. 'Here, listen to this pal. Tommy claims that M.M. is a film star, but not Marilyn.'

Tommy spoke up. 'M.M. is a film star – Marion Morrison. You'll know him as John Wayne.'

'Well, I might be an idiot, but everyone knows that 'Marion' is a lassie's name, in case you hadn't noticed. An' whoever heard o' a man wi' a girl's name?'

They continued in this vein and having been given yet more of the fast-drying toxic material, their behaviour can perhaps be better understood. The fumes were so intense that both contestants had tears streaming from their red, bloodshot eyes. As he left the kitchen area, the young apprentice stopped momentarily to study the pair. They both had tight trousers and identical 'duck's arse' hairstyles. They radiated a devil-may-care attitude, but, unknown to the youngster, they were actually terrified. Their apprenticeship training was nearly complete and very soon they would find themselves qualifying for full adult wages, having to compete with all the other more qualified tradesmen. Secretly, each wished he had paid more attention when being shown the tricks of the trade instead of day-dreaming about the latest Billy Eckstine shirts.

At the other end of the kitchen, unaware of their inner dilemmas, was the restaurant owner. He had removed his jacket, with the hand-stitched lapels, and, together with the waistcoat, he placed them carefully on a hanger and hung them inside a small cubicle adjacent to the work area. This little kiosk was empty, except for a sepia-tinted old photograph of a serious-looking couple; presumably, his paternal grandparents. He pushed his shirt sleeves half-way up his forearms, where they were held by a pair of silver armbands. He did the same with the watch with the expanding gold bracelet. He flamboyantly took a crisp, white-starched apron from a pile nearby and after cracking it like a whip to unfold it, tied it round his middle. Next, he put on a chef's hat at a rakish angle. He pulled out a gold lighter from his shirt pocket and, after a bit of business lighting a cigar, he went along the row of gas ovens and grills – click, click, click, click, click. He placed the cigar on the edge of the sink and set about the task at hand.

On the work surface he placed all the ingredients for the meal; they were arranged, not unlike the paintshop, in rows according to their purpose. Various jars of seasonings were arrayed in order. To his right side he placed a wooden block that housed his professional cooking knives. He winked at the apprentice who was mesmerised by the spectacle, never having seen food prepared by such a showman. The chef pulled a turkey centre stage and with a twist of his wrist had trussed its legs. As he performed these tasks he was quietly singing, then he threw back his head and roared out a snatch of the aria from Tosca at full volume.

The boy thought him the classiest guy he had ever encountered. Reality broke the spell. The foreman whistled (in the style of a boson welcoming an Admiral aboard ship). The men called it the 'painter's whistle', but who could be certain. They kidded the young man so much; this being the only power they had.

The apprentice ran to the whistle, only to be directed by a nod in the direction of the toilets where the new men were working. Well, really it was two nods. One to indicate the material and the other the direction in which it was to be taken. No eye contact played any part in the transaction.

The toilets comprised of three cubicles and a long, tiled urinal. Each cubicle contained a new start. It was understood by all that it was a kind of test case. Their workmanship, cleanliness and speed would be scrutinised surreptitiously by the foreman and anyone deemed to have out-performed the other two could possibly look forward to being kept on through the winter in to spring, when the building trade woke up after its period of hibernation and there was work a-plenty. But this wasn't spring and so, in this deadly game of 'De'il take the hindmost', man was forced to compete against man, whether it was in his nature or not.

Not in the competition though was a simple man, who was fastidiously cleaning the tiled urinal. This was accepted by everyone. He wasn't up to the challenge. In this non-competitive frame of mind he chipped away at the brown, calcified urine stains with his scraper; the same scraper that had earlier in the day been used to half an apple, which he had kindly shared with the young apprentice. Like the owner, this man also sang at the top of his voice as he worked. Tunelessly he belted out something about having the world upon a string sitting on a rainbow.

The boy entered the first cubicle to angry shouts of abuse. The occupant had painted the back of the door and now, on it being opened, his steward's jacket was covered in wet paint. Mumbling an apology, the boy gave the man more paint. He cautiously went next door. This man was smiling, having heard the outburst. The boy nervously topped up the man's paint pot. Only that very morning he had overheard one of the regulars tell the foreman that 'that one is worth a watching'. The man surprised him by thanking him on the refill. Almost no-one thanked him and it calmed him a little. Knocking the last door, not wishing to repeat his earlier mistake, he heard the occupant say that not only was he welcome to join him inside, but it would be a pleasure and he would introduce him to an old friend of his as well.

The boy suspected something wasn't quite right, but he had to deliver the paint, come what may. He pushed open the door. There stood the new man, overalls at his ankles, prick in hand.

'He's my best friend' said the man. 'Come in. He won't bite'.

The apprentice blushed and stammered something along the lines of the man should act his age. He couldn't be certain of what he had said, being in a bit of a state. He was secretly glad the man who was 'worth a watching' was nearby.

The owner was now standing at the kitchen door, from which came such a tempting aroma. It intimated the pleasures to come and even through the stench of toxic fumes the saliva juices of the painters began to flow.

The regulars in the main restaurant had got themselves cleaned after a fashion and were now waiting to be told what to do. These battle-hardened heroes were afraid to sit down until instructed to do so by the foreman.

The long table was dramatically lit, the owner having now dimmed the main lights highlighting only the table in a pool of light.

The foreman, taking his cue from the owner, nodded to the men. Game on.

The painters noisily took their places at the table. There was lots of pushing and good-natured insults being shared. They pulled crackers with each other and from them put on paper crowns – kings for a day! They blew up balloons, read banal parables and shouted out the feeble jokes that the crackers contained. They laughed uproariously, as if the jokes were freshly minted and that they were hearing them for the first time.

Aggie was great with the men; pulling crackers with most of them. Many were old friends, having shared a few Christmases together. She was generous with her affections and flirted innocently with each and every one. She laughed at some of the jokes; others, in poor taste, she just ignored.

The owner, to loud applause, approached the table carrying a large roasted turkey on a silver tray. He carried it aloft with panache, his sweating face glowing above his hand-tied bow tie.

Aggie and him now proceeded to serve the men. The painters were deferential, having experienced the ritual in the services, when at Christmas dinners the officers served the other ranks. They appreciated the gesture and applauded the owner for his magnanimity.

Having filled up the men's glasses, the owner rattled a spoon against a glass for attention. Silence. He then arose and proposed a toast:

'To this magnificent country of ours. To our dear Royal Family and especially our beautiful young Queen Elizabeth the Second. And let us also give thanks to God that we live in this the freest country in the world.'

Everyone did as requested, except for the young apprentice. It might have gone unnoticed, but one of the gathering, for whatever reason, brought it to the attention of the foreman. He, in turn, pointed it out to the owner, giving an exaggerated apology for the boy's social ineptitude and downright bad manners.

The owner turned to the boy. 'Does my toast not suit you?' Shaking his head he sat down. There was a pause, then quietly the boy spoke.

'I'm not familiar with any other countries and their level of freedom, but, although I'm young, I know a little of what goes on in this country. How men can't find a full year's work. I also know that I'll soon be called up to do my National Service and I'll possibly be sent to our colonies to make sure they don't share in any of our freedoms.'

The owner jumped to his feet. 'Leave politics out of it, please.' Then his face flushed with anger. 'Surely you'll toast our Queen?'

'She's not my Queen' replied the boy. 'And anyhow, she should really be Elizabeth the *First* of Scotland.'

Raging, the owner moved in for the kill. 'You sound very much like a communist and, if I'm not mistaken, that usually means you're an atheist and therefore you don't celebrate Christmas. If that's the case, kindly leave the table and let us enjoy ourselves.'

The boy was out of his depth and he knew it. He stared back in silence, and then got up from the table. The foreman jabbed a finger towards the shadows.

The boy stood outside the pool of light. The men resumed the banter and cracker pulling. The boy felt the loneliness that being an outsider means. To be expelled from any group is awful; to be excluded from one's workmates is wretched. He held back the tears. Any evidence of that and he would be finished forever. He was hungry, but not for the contents of the table, wonderful as they were. No, he was hungry for human contact.

One of the new men rose and beckoned the boy. 'Here, have mine, son. I'm not hungry anyway. Maybe it's the paint fumes, but I'd rather have a smoke.'

The owner turned to address the new start. 'You're making a mistake, man. Didn't you hear the boy? He never answered when I accused him of being an atheist. This is a Christmas dinner, and he doesn't believe in it.'

'Do you?' replied the new start.

'That's beside the point, and well out of order' raged the owner.

Everyone looked at their dinner plates. No one wanted to attract any attention to themselves. You don't need this. Not now. Not in these difficult times.

'Well, I, and many others, fought a war so that people like you could exercise their freedom of speech. People should be able to hold opinions that you may yourself find unpleasant. I know that if the events we've just witnessed had taken place down the pub many round this table would have had a point of view and voiced it.'

The owner, used to serving the public, capitulated quickly. 'You're right, of course. I was only having a joke with the lad. He knows that.' He theatrically cupped his hand to his ear and without looking at the apprentice said 'Son, just say you were wrong and we can all enjoy our dinner – you included.'

The boy stared from his position beyond the pale.

'Can't hear you, son' roared the owner, now back in control. The boy was in a spot.

The new man leapt in again. 'Don't answer, son.' Then turning to address the owner he spoke in a clear, angry voice. 'I was a guest of the Germans for a few years and I know what it's like to be utterly powerless. It's a feeling you never forget. You, sir, have all the power in this little scene being played out here. That boy has none. Give in. It's only a laugh, eh?'

The foreman was now on his feet. 'You're wasting this for all of us. I'll not forget it in a hurry.'

The new man lifted his plate and brought it over to the young apprentice. In doing so, he knew he had blown his chance of being kept on through the winter.

The silence round the table was unbearable in its intensity. The men toyed with their food. They didn't welcome controversy, but neither did they like what they all knew the boy was experiencing. They moved the food around their plates, but not a forkful made it up to their mouths. The two older apprentices pretended to be so engrossed in a game of nipping one another that they were oblivious to what was going on around them. In truth, the twosome heard every word and, as a consequence, both their plates remained untouched. The other new starts shovelled the food into their mouths - one because he had been unemployed since the previous month, the other because he could not have cared less. And the simple man? He was just hungry.

Then, just as everyone thought that the high water mark had been reached and a tranquil time lay ahead, it happened. Aggie entered the fray. She threw her paper hat at the owner.

'That wee boy's right' she said. 'I was about that age when I started here wi' your Dad. I was only going to work until I got married, but Thomas never came back frae France. I'm no' complaining. I wisnae alone, thousands of poor lassies were in the same position as me. We a' accepted oor lot. Same as the young soldiers at the time. I was serving in your smoke lounge full wi' a' the businessmen. Sons o' the rich, maist o' them. It couldnae be co-incidence, could it? I thought a lot aboot it, but I had my work tae dae, so I put it a' in the back o' my mind. They were a doin' nicely oot o' the war. Cannae blame them, though. That was how the cards had been dealt. Many a night I went hame tae my Mither's, an' when she had gone to bed I had a wee greet at what might have been.

'The war ended. We had years o' bad times, but it was still the same faces in the smoke lounge – older, married wi' kids. They treated me well. It was Aggie this, and Aggie that, and they tipped well tae.'

'Well, there you are, Aggie. It's not been so bad, eh?' said the baffled owner.

'Then came the last war' continued Aggie. 'Same faces, same deals getting made, same old story. A good investment tae be made here – a good killing there. I heard everything, but kept ma mooth shut. But that's when I became a Trotskyist!'

'But Aggie. Aggie, you're family' said the owner in utter amazement.

'Family? That's another thing. You haven't got the character of your old man. He at least knew how fortunate it was that the family got oot o' Lithuania.'

She untied her apron and that was now hurled at the owner. He caught it and absent-mindedly folded it and put it on his knee.

Aggie continued. Next came the starched cuffs. 'Stick those where the sun don't shine. I've given your family my entire life and in a' ma years working here I never saw anything as beautiful as what that man did today.'

She turned towards the new man and, standing to attention, gave him the red, clenched-fist salute.

'Comrade, you showed us all what Christmas should really be about. I hope you have a long and prosperous life. You're a good man.'

She turned and without looking back went out the front door and was gone.

The owner sighed deeply, got up, removed his paper hat and, on some pretext or other, returned to the kitchen. The laughter slowly returned to the table, quiet at first then, by degrees, louder and louder, until it was the noisiest dinner party any of them could remember. The foreman sat alone eating in silence. He had also served his boss all his life. Would anything he had just heard alter his conduct? It was hard to guess, but a good clue was that periodically he looked at his watch, keen to get started. Work he at least understood.

The apprentice was now seated at the table, pulling a cracker with one of the squad. Everybody there was in awe of spirited old Aggie. The boy looked over at the new man, who was casually rolling a cigarette trying to avoid any form of contact with the foreman.

The apprentice noted everything. He vaguely understood. The journey was going to be exciting.

Starrett on Italy

La Dolce Vita – a letter from Bob Starrett

Dear Rick

By now you'll have seen by the postmark that I'm living in Italy. Why? Well, it's one of those events that take place in my life periodically, between long periods of routine behaviour. I'll call it artistic temperament (Wee Boab isn't as constrained as his west of Scotland Calvinistic background would have people believe).

The truth of the matter is that for more years than I want to think about I've always wanted to spend a bit of time in this part of the world – artwise… Well, an Italian comrade visited the Byres Road during the summer and I asked if there was anything doing that I could handle.

I forgot all about it…

However, a couple of weeks back he sent for me with, as they say, an offer I couldn't refuse. It's guarding an ancient villa full of neo-classical junk that's awaiting auction in about a year's time. I've to wander through the junk-filled rooms at night and check the seals on the doors. It takes a bit of getting used to. But patrolling the grounds at night is the experience of all time. Being a city slicker I had always assumed that night time in the country was fairly quiet. Well, have you ever heard an acorn CRASH to the ground in the dead of night? Not to mention autumn leaves following you around, being blown by a slight breeze that wheezes in fits and starts like an old man. Aye, Rick, in times like these I'm glad I'm a Marxist. As for robbers, well, I'm armed with a Winchester Repeater, and at times I would rather face robbers, at least they're from the materialistic world; whereas the dark side of nature is beyond my ken.

Which brings me to a subject that should interest you. Because of the language difficulties (the inflections, the dialects, the hand language, etc.) it's a constant strain to listen to everyday conversation. Indeed, it's like experiencing a deluge of words and you're trying to catch one drop as a starting point. The outcome of it is that one's senses are heightened to such a degree that it's like hearing words for the first time in one's life. In just such a frame of mind, I read Hugh MacDiarmid's *Drunk Man Looks etc*… It was knock-out. Whereas previously I had skimmed the surface of the words, with my new awareness of their sounds, meanings, etc. the poem was a real emotional experience. Imagine having to travel to Italy to understand one's own language!

A wee bit of spiel about my position here. Seeing so much beauty after seven-and-a-half years looking at bloody war ships is too strong a diet. I went out last Sunday with a comrade and the first little hamlet we passed through was absolutely beautiful, so much so that I wanted to photograph it right away. Then we passed another of different style, but equally beautiful and another and another and another… It was visually the equivalent of a kid being let loose in a sweet shop, and the feeling of nausea was just as strong at the end of the day. On TV last year, during a three-part series about a dreadful housing estate in Glasgow – Lilybank, a councillor remarked that 'there was pain felt by so long looking at downright grey ugliness'. Well, I have just the opposite. We dined on trout antipasto, trout spaghetti, roasted trout… I hadn't had a trout in years (too expensive in Scotland) and here we were eating them in surroundings of indescribable beauty (the mountain peaks were all capped with snow a la tourist posters) and everyone round the table a communist. I remarked on the difference in lifestyles between our two countries and, indeed, between our two parties. They laughed – hedonists to a man. This is not the home of the Dolce Vita for nought!

Everyone is armed to the bloody teeth. The bastards shoot everything that takes to the air. Someone said that 'you could judge the freedom of a country by the right of the populace to bear arms'. It's some contradiction.

This region has one of the highest living standards in Europe. My own wages are fantastic. Food is cheap as it's an agricultural area. Someone told me that the place had the highest amount of motor cars per capita in Italia. Well, they didn't need to tell me, really – I had already attempted unsuccessfully to cross the road!

Now, I hope to continue working with Brian and yourself, Rick, but there may be a difficulty getting my brain sorted out to do any decent work. My cartoons depend on being abrasive and it's a difficult emotion to generate after you've dined on a five-course meal. But it's my wish – one would have to take into account the Italian postal service, which must be the worst in the world. But given plenty of time we should be able to work something out.

I was getting myself fit before departing and, as you know, you don't want to lose the fitness once you have attained it – it's too bloody hard-earned. I was enquiring about bringing a racing bike over here and, honestly, the faces on the guys registered complete bafflement. Why anyone would want to push their bodies through any kind of hardship was beyond them. A comrade, Renzo, who organises a cycle race annually for the town, told me that all the leading cycle racers argue over the course, the amount of prize money, etc., and he told me, to a man, they all hate the game. They hope to win a few quid and open a wee factory or something. The guys he mentioned are my idols too!!

The illustrations I've included, Rick, maybe will be too parochial for your readers, but they accurately reflect the position of a shipyard punter facing new experiences.

The illustration showing me at a typical Italian table is based on a visit I made to a farm house in the village of Petriolo. It was typical Italian and the people had worked the land for years, as their people did before them. Indeed, the house itself was at least 200 years old. There were party members of long-standing and I looked for the usual 'clues' to back that up. But it was all so very different from back home. The telly had a curtain round it, like a theatre (which is maybe the idea) and I've included that in the sketch. From the ceiling clung all kinds of salamis, etc. and yet the only visual on the walls, which were all stark white, was a print of Mickey Mouse. I've entitled the illustration 'Cultural Imperialism', but you know all that.

The drawing depicting me as a prisoner of the Villa is near the mark as to what a creative person feels when, for one reason or another, they can't 'take part' or fully understand their environment.

I see Voices still has cash difficulties. Aye, the UK is free all right – if you have the dough. But it's one of the few publications that exist for workers to express themselves which isn't infantile, so it must survive.

Your aye

Bob

Doon Through The Years

Words: Arthur Johnstone. Tune: Nicky Tams (Trad.)

I've worked for over forty years
Frae Fairfield's doon tae Broon's.
I've even worked the tail o' the bank
Wi' the lads frae Greenock Toon.
I've been on trials on the measured mile
Noo I've done it a' wi' pride
For I've helped tae build the giant ships
That sail the oceans wide.

When we built the new Q4
It was a mighty sight.
There was electricians, engineers
And even the odd shipwright.
There was Harry the Horse, who selt us tools:
The best American brand.
He said he got them frae New York,
But his story didnae stand.

I was working back in Fairfield's
When the word was passed aroon:
The Government was shuttin' doon
A' the yairds in Glesga Toon.
They said oor yairds they didnae pay
And we would have tae go.
But the men all stood together
And we proudly answered: 'No'.

Jimmy Reid and Airlie
Barr, Gilmour and the rest.
They a' went doon tae London Toon
The Government tae face.
They telt them we were workin' in,
That we were gaun tae stay.
When the Government relented
UCS had won the day.

As I look back doon through the years
At the changes we have seen
They're building a' they yuppie flats
A' the way tae Glesga Green.
But the Govan lads are working on
And Yarrow's seems awright.
But I hate tae think whit might have been
If we hidnae put up that fight.

Showing A Way

In Celebration and Consideration of the UCS Work-in 1971-72

'We are witnessing an eruption not of lava but of labour. The labour of working men and women...'

JIMMY REID,
Glasgow Green, 18 August 1971

Once upon a time,
and in the hard, real world -
for this is not fairy tale – here,
on the banks of Scotland's Clyde,
a bold idea transmuted If to That,
and Just imagine, acted on by many,
took on the force of hard material fact.
This happened forty years ago.
The wonder is, given the world's wars since,
and the wounds received, the bold idea
has not yet died.

All rivers have their storied past,
in part the same, in part unique.
More than a few have known the pride
of ships well-made and safely launched;
and also known, when fortunes ebb,
a shadow-side. But here, at UCS, in '71,
a short-lived Labour hegemony was ours;
while Capital, out-classed, endured

a turning from its wrecking plan,
with loosening powers.

The reason is not hard to seek: big
on any scale, a volcano, not of lava
but of Labour, burst in flame.
That is the core and focus
of our special claim. The action
that eight thousand shipyard workers took
filled awhile the skies of politics.
Briefly, social order's deep assumptions
shook.

Lame duck, said Capital, despising
and dismissive of the Clydebank yards.
Never mind the lives invested there,
the teeming skills, the order book!
Never mind the hinterland they served,
that equally in turn served them!
Dead duck was what their enemies wished
to see, little knowing that our bird would fly,
and fly, deriving strength from thousands,
then from tens of thousands,
and their solidarity.

Unite and fight! In tandem, and in full,
heeding the maxim's dual elements,
'fight' and 'unite', not from the dole
outwith the shipyards' gates, but working

from within: there lay the workers' stratagem,
that helped us win.

The shipyards' mail bag,
like a farmer's sack of seed, spilled out
its daily bulge of contents: news received
of rallies, demonstrations, strikes;
well-wishers' words, and sometimes flowers;
and cash, from corner shops, from churches,
children, unions, and the whole wide listening world,
sums both large and widows' generous mites -
sent in comradeship, to keep
the struggle's fire alight.

We thought our cause victorious.
The bold idea, in act, in fact, had proved
its worth: the yards were saved.
But now, four decades on, what's left?
In place of gain, a creeping dearth!
Not only ships have sunk, or gone for scrap,
but yards as well, and jobs, and skills,
and with them, hope. Along the river,
as throughout the land, and world,
we feel a cutting wind that kills.
Economics winter has us in its grip.

For Capital, the battle that we won in '71
was clarion-call and school; it learned
for more than we. It learned to hone

its tools of shock, displace, lay off, and rule.
Ganging up and doing down,
it made too many of us settle, first for slices
of the proverbial loaf, then beggars' crusts,
then bugger all. Ruthlessly,
It grasped again its habitual crown.

For us, a tragedy ensued, its playing-out
still under way: comrades at loggerheads
and each others' throats; lost sense of purpose
and of common cause, confusion
and the side-track having won the day;
unions and parties pulled apart,
taking the line of least, not most resistance
in a losing war. What should -
what could – we have attempted otherwise,
or more?

Can we revive and build afresh
that bold idea that found a shape and home
at UCS? Can we re-launch it
on the carrying stream of people's needs
and dearest dreams? Can we extend it
to the point it captures greater powers,
and thus rebuts, with allies everywhere,
the might that Capital will bring to bear?

Present struggle cries to learn
the complex story of its past.

Take it! Save it from erasure,
or revision's grasp!
What happened here, in '71,
can be no Terra nullius of the mind,
open for errors to invade.
It's where we entered history,
and showed a way whereby a future
might be made.

Hand written on the first page 'David Betteridge August, 2010'